W9-CPV-889

THE CHILDHOOD OF FAMOUS AMERICANS SERIES

By CHARLOTTA M. BEBENROTH
Meriwether Lewis: Boy Explorer

By BERNICE BRYANT
Dan Morgan: Boy of the Wilderness

By CONSTANCE BUEL BURNETT
Lucretia Mott: Girl of Old Nantucket

By OLIVE W. BURT
Luther Burbank: Boy Wizard
John Wanamaker: Boy Merchant
Young Jed Smith: Westering Boy

By ELECTA CLARK
Robert Peary: Boy of the North

By SUE GUTHRIDGE
Tom Edison: Boy Inventor

By MARIE HAMMONTREE
Will and Charlie Mayo: Doctor's Boys

By MARGUERITE HENRY
Robert Fulton: Boy Craftsman

By HELEN BOYD HIGGINS
Alec Hamilton: The Little Lion
Stephen Foster: Boy Minstrel
Juliette Low: Girl Scout

By JANE MOORE HOWE
Amelia Earhart: Kansas Girl

By LAURA LONG
Oliver Hazard Perry: Boy of the Sea
David Farragut: Boy Midshipman
George Dewey: Vermont Boy

By MIRIAM E. MASON
Mark Twain: Boy of Old Missouri
Young Audubon: Boy Naturalist
William Penn: Friendly Boy
Mary Mapes Dodge: Jolly Girl
Dan Beard: Boy Scout

By GRACE HATHAWAY MELIN
Maria Mitchell: Girl Astronomer

By MINNIE BELLE MITCHELL
Hoosier Boy: James Whitcomb Riley

By HELEN ALBEE MONSELL
Boy of Old Virginia: Robert E. Lee
Tom Jefferson: A Boy in Colonial Days
Young Stonewall: Tom Jackson
Dolly Madison: Quaker Girl
Henry Clay: Mill Boy of the Slashes
John Marshall: Boy of Young America
Woodrow Wilson: Boy President
Susan Anthony: Girl Who Dared

By AILEEN WELLS PARKS
Davy Crockett: Young Rifleman
Bedford Forrest: Boy on Horseback

By EDD WINFIELD PARKS
Teddy Roosevelt: All-Round Boy

By HOWARD PECKHAM
William Henry Harrison: Young Tippecanoe

By FLORA WARREN SEYMOUR
Bird Girl: Sacagawea
Pocahontas: Brave Girl

By BRADFORD SMITH
William Bradford: Pilgrim Boy
Dan Webster: Union Boy

By DOROTHEA J. SNOW
Eli Whitney: Boy Mechanic
John Paul Jones: Salt-Water Boy
Raphael Semmes: Tidewater Boy

By WILLIAM O. STEELE
John Sevier: Pioneer Boy
Francis Marion: Young Swamp Fox

. . . continued on next page

THE CHILDHOOD OF FAMOUS AMERICANS SERIES—Continued

By AUGUSTA STEVENSON

Abe Lincoln: Frontier Boy
Ben Franklin: Printer's Boy
Andy Jackson: Boy Soldier
George Washington: Boy Leader
Daniel Boone: Boy Hunter
Sam Houston: Boy Chieftain
George Carver: Boy Scientist
Kit Carson: Boy Trapper
Paul Revere: Boy of Old Boston
Clara Barton: Girl Nurse
U. S. Grant: Young Horseman
Buffalo Bill: Boy of the Plains
Anthony Wayne: Daring Boy
Myles Standish: Adventurous Boy
Booker T. Washington: Ambitious Boy
Wilbur and Orville Wright: Boys with Wings
Molly Pitcher: Girl Patriot
Zeb Pike: Boy Traveler
Nancy Hanks: Kentucky Girl

By GUERNSEY VAN RIPER, JR.

Lou Gehrig: Boy of the Sand Lots
Will Rogers: Young Cowboy
Knute Rockne: Young Athlete
Babe Ruth: Baseball Boy

By JEAN BROWN WAGONER

Louisa Alcott: Girl of Old Boston
Jane Addams: Little Lame Girl

By JEAN BROWN WAGONER—cont.

Julia Ward Howe: Girl of Old New York
Martha Washington: Girl of Old Virginia
Abigail Adams: A Girl of Colonial Days

By ANN SPENCE WARNER

Narcissa Whitman: Pioneer Girl

By ANN WEIL

John Quincy Adams: Boy Patriot
Franklin Roosevelt:
    Boy of the Four Freedoms
Betsy Ross: Girl of Old Philadelphia

By MABEL CLELAND WIDDEMER

Washington Irving: Boy of Old New York
Aleck Bell: Ingenious Boy
Harriet Beecher Stowe: Connecticut Girl
Peter Stuyvesant: Boy with Wooden Shoes

By KATHARINE E. WILKIE

Zack Taylor: Young Rough and Ready
Will Clark: Boy in Buckskins
Mary Todd Lincoln: Girl of the Bluegrass

By GERTRUDE HECKER WINDERS

James Fenimore Cooper:
    Leatherstocking Boy
Jim Bowie: Boy with a Hunting Knife
Ethan Allen: Green Mountain Boy

BETSY ROSS

Girl of Old Philadelphia

8.48

BY

ANN WEIL

ILLUSTRATED BY

Sandra James

THE BOBBS-MERRILL COMPANY, INC.

Publishers

INDIANAPOLIS   NEW YORK

To
Susan and Jill

CONTENTS

LIST OF FULL-PAGE ILLUSTRATIONS

BETSY ROSS

Girl of Old Philadelphia

I

WHICH DO YOU CHOOSE?

Betsy Griscom looked up and down the long table. Sitting around it were her father and mother, her six older sisters, her little brother George, and herself. Martha, who was two, and the baby, six months old, had already been fed and put to bed.

Betsy looked around the table and counted each person carefully. "Ten," she said. "Ten people." Then she looked very puzzled. "What will we do, Father," she asked, "when Martha and the baby are old enough to sit at the table? There is just room enough for the ten of us now. Where will we put them?"

Mr. Griscom smiled. "We have always found room at the table for our children, Betsy. I suppose we will find room for Martha and the baby, too."

"I am glad thee is a carpenter, Father," said George. "Thee is the best in all Philadelphia. Thee can build a new table for us when we need one."

"Father doesn't make furniture," said Sarah, who was twelve. "Father builds buildings."

"Thee could make furniture, too, if thee wanted to, couldn't thee, Father?" George was sure his father could do anything.

Mr. Griscom laughed. "I suppose I will have to make a new table whether I want to or not," he said. "Betsy is right. We are about to outgrow this one. We'll have a new one before 1758 is over."

"Good," Betsy said, pleased. "We'll have it this year."

"I'll help thee, Father." George sat up very straight. He was only five years old, but since he was the only boy in the family he felt very important.

"I'll help thee, too, Father." Betsy raised her shoulders as high as she could. She was a year older than George. If he could help, she could too.

George laughed. "Thee cannot make furniture."

"Why not?"

"Thee is a girl. Girls don't make furniture."

"I can make furniture if I want to."

"Thee cannot. Thee is a girl and thee is too little."

Betsy didn't know what to say to George. Being a girl and being little all at the same time was very difficult. She looked down at her plate. Then she had an idea. "I could make doll furniture," she said.

"Doll furniture!" George laughed again. He forgot that sometimes he liked to play with Betsy's dolls, too. He was trying to act very grown-up. "Doll furniture doesn't count."

"It does, too, count!" Betsy looked down toward the far end of the table. "It does, doesn't it, Mother?"

"Of course." Mrs. Griscom smiled at Betsy. "Thee could make doll furniture—size isn't important. Sometimes small things are more difficult to make than large ones. It is how well thee does things that matters. Good work comes in all sizes."

"And little girls come in all sizes, too," said Mr. Griscom, smiling at his seven daughters. "Don't worry, Betsy. Thee will grow up fast enough."

As soon as dinner was over Betsy and George carried all the dishes from the table out to the kitchen. Rachel and Hannah swept the floor and straightened the room. Debby and Susan washed the dishes. Mary and Sarah dried them.

"There!" George picked up the last plate just as Betsy picked up the last bowl. "We're all

After dinner the children went to their tasks.

through, Betsy. Let's go outside and play."

"No." Betsy shook her head.

"Why not?" George asked. He was puzzled.

"I'm not going to play."

"Not going to play?" George repeated. "What is thee going to do?"

Betsy tossed her head. "I'm going to make a table for my doll."

George laughed. "That is foolish. Thee cannot make a table. Thee is too little."

"I am not." Betsy stamped her foot. "Thee will see. I will make a very nice table."

"All right." George turned around and ran to the door. "Thee can stay inside and make a silly old table if thee wants to. I'm going outside and play."

Betsy watched George until he was out of sight. Then she went out the back door, ran down a little brick path and opened the door to her father's workshop.

Inside everything was neat and orderly. All of Mr. Griscom's tools hung on pegs around the room. There were saws and hammers. There were—— Betsy stared at the other tools. She had never looked at them closely before. She didn't know what they were called or how they were used.

Betsy was glad George wasn't with her. She was sure he would know the names and uses of all the tools. She could hear him saying, "Of course thee would not know carpentry. Thee is a girl, and girls don't know about such things."

Betsy walked around the little shed slowly. "Well, at least I know what a saw is used for," she said to herself, "and that's what I need."

Betsy went over to a saw, but she was too short to reach the handle. By standing on tiptoe she could just manage to reach the blade. My, how heavy it was! Betsy took hold of the blade with both hands and pushed. Finally she was able to lift it high enough so that the handle was free from the peg.

The big blade bent. It made a low whining sound. The handle swung out and down. It hit Betsy on top of her head.

"Oh!" Betsy dropped the saw. It fell to the floor, whining some more. It sounded as if it were saying, "Theeeee is a gi-rrrr-lllll. A gi-rrrrr-llllll. Gi-rrrrrr-llllll. Rrrrrr-llllll."

Betsy stood for a few minutes rubbing her head. Then she picked up the saw and put it on her father's workbench. She wasn't going to let a bump on the head stop her. She had to show George she could make a table.

In one corner of the workshop there was a large pile of scrap wood. Betsy liked this corner best. She and George had spent many hours there, playing with the blocks of wood. They built stores and houses and schools. They built wagons and boats. They built huge towers that went up and up and up—and then in one second came tumbling down.

The woodpile was wonderful because it changed every day. Sometimes the pieces were short and thick. Sometimes they were long and narrow. Today they were a grand mixture of big and little, fat and thin.

Betsy wished she didn't have to make a table. It would be more fun to build a house out of all those wonderful pieces of wood before her father took them away. "But I *have* to build a table," she said to herself. "I *have* to show George that I can."

Betsy picked up a thin, flat piece of wood and took it over to the workbench. Then she took the saw in her right hand. She placed it on top of the wood, as she had seen her father do. But the saw was heavy. It wiggled and turned when she tried to hold it. When she tried to work it back and forth across the wood, it refused to move. The sharp teeth bit into the wood and stayed there. No matter how she tugged or pulled, it did no good.

Betsy worked and worked. Finally the saw teeth began to give a little. Then—*zip!*—the saw jumped from the board to Betsy's finger.

"Oh!" Once more the saw went tumbling to

the ground. And once more it seemed to whine, "Theeeee is a gi-rrrr-lllll. A gi-rrrrr-llllll. Gi-rrrrrr-llllll. Rrrrrr-llllll."

Betsy looked at her bleeding finger. Then she turned around, ran out of the shop, down the path and into the house. "Look, Mother!" Betsy held up her bleeding finger for her mother to see.

"Betsy! What happened, child?"

Betsy's eyes flashed. "That old saw! It bit me."

Mrs. Griscom looked as if she were swallowing a smile. She cleared her throat. "Saw? Betsy, what was thee doing with a saw?"

"Making a table for my doll."

"But, Betsy, thee does not know how to use a saw."

"Thee said I could make doll furniture. Thee did. At dinner."

"Oh, dear!" Mrs. Griscom opened a cabinet drawer and took out a clean piece of linen. She tore off a long, narrow strip. She began to wrap it around Betsy's finger. "I know I did, Betsy," she said, "but I did not think thee would try to use the saw. A saw is nothing for a little girl to play with."

Betsy hadn't cried when the saw hit her head. She hadn't even cried when her finger was cut. But when her mother said "little girl," the tears rolled down her cheeks. "Every time I want to do something," she said, "I can't do it because I'm a girl, or because I'm too little. Little girls can't do *anything*!"

Mrs. Griscom tore the end of the bandage in half. She twisted it neatly and tied a knot. "Does thee really want to use a saw?" she asked.

Betsy looked surprised. "Of course I do," she said. "George says——"

"I'm not talking about George," Mrs. Griscom said firmly. "I'm talking about a little girl named Betsy. Does *she* want to use a saw?"

Betsy thought of the whining old saw that had hit her over the head and bitten her finger. Perhaps it wasn't so exciting after all. "Well——" she began.

Mrs. Griscom smiled. "Sit thee down for a minute," she said. "I will be right back."

Betsy wondered what her mother was going to do. She could hear her going down the hall and up the steps. She heard a drawer open and close. Then she heard her mother come down the stairs, through the hall again and back into the kitchen.

Mrs. Griscom walked across the room and sat down beside Betsy. "Hold up thy hands," she said, "and close thy eyes until I say 'Ready.'"

Betsy closed her eyes tightly. She felt something touch the first finger on her right hand.

"Ready!"

Betsy opened her eyes and stared. There on her finger was a beautiful silver thimble.

"Mother!" she cried. "Oh, Mother, it's beautiful!"

Mrs. Griscom smiled. "My mother gave it to me when I was six years old," she said. "It was too large for me then, just as it is too large for thee now. But I grew into it, and so will thee. Now—" Mrs. Griscom held both of Betsy's hands up in front of her—"we have two hands and they are like two different people.

"The left hand," she went on, "is like a girl who is always trying to be someone else. This girl wants to be a boy, or she wants to be older, or she wants to be like someone down the street. She does things she doesn't like to do just because someone else does them. She never does them well and she is always getting into trouble.

"The right hand," Mrs. Griscom continued, "is like a different kind of girl. She doesn't waste time wishing for things that can never be. She

"Which hand does thee like the better?" Mrs. Griscom asked.

does what she likes to do and so does them well. This person is happy just being herself."

Mrs. Griscom looked at Betsy. "Which hand does thee like the better?" she asked.

Betsy looked at her left hand with the white bandage on the first finger. The ends of the knot stood up like little bunny ears that seemed to be wiggling at her. Having a bandage on her finger made her feel a little different and rather important. But underneath her finger throbbed and hurt. It wasn't very comfortable.

Betsy looked at her right hand with the thimble on the first finger. When she moved her finger back and forth the thimble swung to and fro like a little silver bell. It looked gay and inviting.

Betsy thought of all the times she had begged her mother to let her sew. Perhaps she was old enough now. She thought of all the things she wanted to make. Doll clothes were much more fun than doll furniture.

Betsy looked up at her mother and smiled. "I'll take the right hand," she said. "I *am* glad I'm me. I'll never try to be someone else again."

II

THE MYSTERY OF THE SOUR DOUGH

BAKING DAY! When Betsy woke the next morning she could almost imagine that a delicious odor filled the house. But she was glad she couldn't smell the golden, crusty loaves baking. That would have meant she was too late.

Betsy dressed quickly and ran down the stairs to the kitchen. This was her favorite day of the week. It was the one day, too, when she was glad she was both little and a girl. Had she been older she would have gone off to school with her older sisters. And if she had been a boy, like George, she wouldn't have been able to help her mother with the baking.

George, too, liked to be in the kitchen on baking day. He watched Betsy as she climbed up on her stool beside her mother.

Mrs. Griscom had mixed the dough early in

Mrs. Griscom and Betsy began to knead the dough.

the morning. She and Betsy began to knead it after breakfast. They patted the dough into mounds. Then they stretched the dough, doubled it over into a mound again and pressed it with the palms of their hands.

George leaned against the kitchen table and watched them. He wished he could work with the dough, too. "Please." He moved a little closer to the kneading trough. "Please, may I help?"

Mrs. Griscom shook her head. "Baking is for girls. And boys, if they want to watch, shouldn't get in the way."

Betsy looked down at George from her high stool. He could have the workshop and all the tools. Baking was much more fun than sawing and hammering. She liked to feel the dough in her hands. It was as soft and silky as a piece of cloth.

They had almost finished when the baby began

to cry. "Oh, dear." Mrs. Griscom hurried out of the room. "The dough is almost ready," she called back to Betsy. "Knead it a little longer and then put it to rise. And don't forget the sour dough," she added as she hurried up the stairs.

Betsy nodded to herself. She couldn't forget the sour dough. That was her favorite part of baking day.

When Mrs. Griscom mixed the dough for the week, she always put a little bit aside. Betsy knew that this was so that yeast could grow in the dough. This was very important—if they didn't have yeast, they wouldn't have bread. They'd have only dough that wouldn't rise.

Betsy always liked to hear her mother tell how she had brought a bit of sour dough from her mother's house to her new home after she was married. Betsy knew that her mother's mother had done the same thing.

"Just think," Betsy would say. "Week after

week, year after year, a bit of dough has been
saved. It links together all the bread that has
been made in thy family since they came to
America."

No, Betsy couldn't forget the sour dough. She
took out a handful, formed it into a little round
ball and put it down on the table.

She gave the dough in the kneading trough
one more pat and covered it carefully with a
piece of white cloth. The wooden trough looked
like a cradle. As Betsy tucked the cloth around
it she felt as if she were putting a baby to bed.

"There." Betsy looked at George and smiled.
"I can play with thee for a little while now." She
took off her apron and hung it on a peg. "I can
play until the dough has risen."

George was glad to play, but playing with
Betsy on baking day wasn't very much fun. She
kept running back into the kitchen to look at
the dough.

"It will never rise if you keep uncovering it all the time," George said finally. He felt very impatient with her.

Betsy tossed her head. "Boys don't understand about baking," she said. "If it rises too much or too little the bread won't be good."

At last Betsy and her mother both agreed that the dough was just right. They spent the afternoon shaping it into huge loaves and baking them in the oven. Finally the last golden, crispy loaf was put on the big dining table to cool.

Betsy ran off to play with George again, and Mrs. Griscom began to put the kitchen in order. Finally the dishes were washed, the worktable was scraped clean and the floor was swept.

"Betsy!" Mrs. Griscom went to the kitchen door and called across the yard. "Betsy, where did thee put the sour dough? I'm ready to put it in the cellar."

"It's on the table!" Betsy shouted. "Right beside the kneading trough!"

A few minutes later Mrs. Griscom went to the kitchen door again. "I can't find it, Betsy," she called. "I've looked everywhere."

Betsy stopped in the middle of a hopping race with George and ran toward the house. "It's right there, Mother. I'm sure it is." She ran into the kitchen, climbed onto her stool and looked down at the table where she had been working. The kneading trough was there, but where was the sour dough?

Once more Mrs. Griscom looked all about the kitchen. Betsy, right behind her, looked everywhere, too. They opened cupboard doors. They looked on the floor, in the flour barrel and even in the wood box. They opened drawers and took out all of Mrs. Griscom's neatly folded towels.

Betsy found a corncob doll that had been missing for a week. Mrs. Griscom found a knife that had fallen between the oven and the worktable. Betsy discovered a loose stone in the hearth. But neither of them found the sour dough.

Betsy looked ready to cry. "Mother, I know I took a piece out. I remember. And I put it right here." Betsy pointed to the table.

Mrs. Griscom smiled. "Sometimes we think so much about something we are sure we did it. Perhaps thee just thought thee took it out."

"But I did. I know I did." There were tears in Betsy's eyes now. "I remember taking it out and putting it right here." Once more she pointed to the table.

"Well, thee mustn't feel too bad about it." Mrs. Griscom put her arm around Betsy. "Mrs. Adams, next door, will be glad to give us a bit of sour dough the next time she bakes. We won't be lacking in bread."

"But Mrs. Adams' bread isn't nearly so good as ours." The tears rolled down Betsy's cheeks.

"Our bread will never taste the same now. Never."

"Why, Betsy! Mrs. Adams bakes very good bread. Anyway, thee knows there is more to good bread than the sour dough. There's the mixing and the kneading and the rising. Thee knows that."

"But that dough belonged to thee—and thy mother—and thy mother's mother." Betsy looked at the freshly baked loaves of bread on the table. "The bread won't *seem* the same even if it tastes the same."

Mrs. Griscom nodded. "It is nice to think of all the bread reaching so far back," she said. "I've often thought of all the hundreds and hundreds of loaves that have risen from that one bit of yeast my grandmother made when she was a young girl. But thee mustn't cry about it, Betsy. It isn't that important."

"But it is! It is!" Betsy felt as if something

very precious had been lost—something no one could ever replace.

A few minutes later Betsy sat up and wiped her eyes. "But, Mother," she said again, "I'm sure I took the dough out. It has to be here in the kitchen. It couldn't have walked away. There was just thee and me and George——"

George!

Betsy remembered that when George was smaller he always begged his mother for a piece of dough. He would knead it and work it and roll it into a ball. The longer he worked the smaller and dirtier it became.

He could never understand why his mother wouldn't bake his bit of dough with the rest of the bread. "It looks fine to me," he always said, looking with pride at the gray ball in his hands.

Now that George was five he felt too old to beg for some dough. But if he had happened to find a piece on the floor——

Betsy ran out of the kitchen and down the path. She knew they wouldn't be able to use the dough if George had been playing with it, but she had to know. "George!" she called. "George, come here a minute."

George hurried toward her.

Betsy looked at him sternly. "George, did thee find a piece of dough on the kitchen floor?"

"No." George looked puzzled.

"It was the sour dough," Betsy explained. "I took a piece out and now it's gone."

George shook his head. "I didn't see it," he said. "Honestly I didn't, Betsy."

Betsy walked slowly back to the kitchen. Had she really taken it out? Perhaps her mother was right. Perhaps she had only thought about it. Tears came to her eyes again.

But Betsy wouldn't give up. Once more she went over every bit of the kitchen. Again she bent down to look over the newly swept floor.

At that moment Mrs. Griscom picked up the kneading trough and started to carry it across the room. Betsy, still on the floor, looked up as her mother passed beside her.

"Mother!" Betsy sat down on the floor and put her head in her lap. "Mother, I——" Her shoulders began to shake.

At first Mrs. Griscom thought she was crying again. Then it sounded as if she were laughing. "Betsy!" Mrs. Griscom put the trough on the table again and knelt beside her. "What ails thee, child? What is the matter?"

"I . . . It . . ." Betsy gasped for breath. She couldn't go on.

Finally she was able to speak. She pointed toward the kneading trough. "Pick it up, Mother," she said. "Please pick it up."

Mrs. Griscom looked puzzled. "What is thee talking about?"

"Pick it up, Mother." Betsy whispered the words. "Then thee will know."

Mrs. Griscom stood up and lifted the trough off the table. Then, still puzzled, she looked down at Betsy.

"Look!" Betsy pointed to the bottom.

Mrs. Griscom raised the trough above her head. "Oh!" Now it was her turn to laugh. There on the bottom of the trough was something white. It was flat and smooth and looked like a new patch.

"Oh, dear." Mrs. Griscom shook her head. "I remember now that I moved the trough over a little bit when I was wiping the table. Of course it's so heavy it mashed the dough flat against the bottom."

Betsy and her mother smiled at each other. The Griscoms would still have bread linked to the hundreds of loaves of bread that had already been baked. The link wasn't broken after all.

III

THE PEPPERMINT STICK

Betsy rubbed her eyes. Then, with a little cry, she jumped out of bed. "It's here!" she cried. "It's really here. I didn't think it would ever come, but it did. It's *the day!*"

Betsy ran to the window and looked out. *The day* was certainly a nice day. It was a warm, sunny September morning in 1759. Below her, on the street, Betsy could see Mr. Grant, who owned the little grocery store on the corner.

"Mr. Grant! Mr. Grant!" She leaned far out on the window sill and waved her hand.

"Betsy!" Mr. Grant stopped, looked up at her and waved, too. "How are you this morning?"

"I am fine, thank thee. And I'm going to school. This is my first day."

"You don't say." Mr. Grant shook a finger

at her. "Now, you be a good girl." Mr. Grant did not say "thee" and "thy" like her Quaker family.

"I will."

"Stop by my store this morning," he said. "I might have a peppermint stick for a little girl on her first day at school."

"I will." Betsy laughed. "Thank thee, Mr. Grant."

"But you mustn't be late." Mr. Grant shook his finger at her again. "You'd better hurry."

"That's right." Betsy turned away from the window and walked across the room. Her new dress and bonnet were spread out on a chair waiting for her. The dress was gray and the bonnet was white. They looked exactly like her old ones.

But Betsy didn't expect them to look different. They were Quaker clothes, and Quaker clothes always looked the same. These were very exciting anyway. These were *new*. With six older sisters Betsy was used to hand-me-downs. This was the first time she had had clothes made especially for her.

The first day of school, a new dress and bonnet, and a peppermint stick! Betsy was so excited she could scarcely dress. This morning when her father left for work and the older girls left for school she would be with them. She wouldn't have to stay home with George and Martha and the baby.

Betsy ran downstairs and into the kitchen. She helped herself to a large bowl of oatmeal and sat down at the table beside George.

"Wish I could go to school." George looked unhappy.

"It won't be long." Betsy felt very grown-up. She remembered when Rachel had said that to her. Now she was saying it to George.

"It will, too, be a long time." George blinked

his eyes and tried to keep from crying. "It will be a whole year."

Betsy patted his arm. "I didn't think the day would ever come, either, but it did. It——"

"Hurry, Betsy! 'Tis late!"

Betsy looked up. Her sisters were ready to leave. "Oh, dear!" She finished her oatmeal quickly. "I have to go now, George. I don't want to be late the very first day."

As Betsy hurried down the walk with her older sisters she saw George standing at the window. His nose was pressed flat against the pane. He looked lonely and forlorn.

Betsy remembered how often she had stood at the window and watched the others go off. She felt very sorry for George.

"Good-by, George." Betsy walked backward and waved to him. "Good-by." She kept waving until they turned the corner. But even then she imagined she could still see his little flat-nosed face in the window.

When the girls got to the end of the street Mr. Grant was waiting outside his store. He held out the peppermint stick and smiled at Betsy. "Here you are, young lady. A present for the first day at school."

"I thank thee very much." Betsy took the peppermint stick and looked at it fondly. She hadn't had one in a long, long time. Just smelling it was wonderful. She could already feel its tingly taste on her tongue. Just as she was ready to pop it into her mouth she thought of George's sad little face.

"Oh!" Without thinking and without a word to anyone Betsy turned around and started to run. Down the street she went, around the corner, up the path and into her house. George was still standing with his nose pressed against the window.

Mr. Grant held out a peppermint stick.

"Here." Betsy thrust the candy into his hand, turned around and ran out again. Down the path she went, around the corner and up the street. Then she stopped.

The corner was deserted. Mr. Grant was inside his store waiting on a customer. Her sisters had vanished.

"Oh dear!" Betsy looked around her. Could she find her way to school? She wasn't sure. Betsy knew the school was on Drinker's Alley. But where was Drinker's Alley? Should she turn right or left or go straight ahead? She wasn't sure.

Betsy looked up and down the street. Then she began to turn around slowly, looking in every direction. Her sisters had gone on without her. She would surely be late.

Then, far in the distance, she saw six objects coming toward her. The six objects turned into six girls. The six girls turned into six sisters.

"Betsy!"

"Where has thee been?"

"What did thee do?"

"We lost thee."

"Where did thee go?"

"We didn't know thee wasn't with us."

Betsy looked from one sister to the other. But she didn't have a chance to answer any of them. Debby took one of her arms and Susan the other. They all began to run.

Betsy ran, too, but most of the time she was running in the air instead of on the ground. Debby and Susan were determined not to be late. They half carried her between them.

"There!" Debby and Susan put Betsy down in the schoolyard and hurried on with Mary and Sarah. The four older girls were too old for Miss Rebecca Jones's school on Drinker's Alley. They went to the large Friends' School on South Fourth Street.

Now Rachel and Hannah were tugging at Betsy. "Come on," they said. "There's Miss Rebecca ready to ring the bell. We have to hurry."

Betsy looked around shyly at all the children in the schoolyard. Then, in a minute, her shyness disappeared. Miss Rebecca's school was a Quaker school and only Quaker children went there. Betsy had seen all of these children at meeting on First Day. They were her friends. "There's Lucy," she said, "and Abby and Ellen and——"

They had reached the school steps and Miss Rebecca was standing at the top looking down at them.

"Gracious, child," she said, looking straight at Betsy, "what happened to thee?"

For the first time Betsy realized that her bonnet was over one eye, her kerchief was turned backward, and her skirt was twisted to one side.

Betsy swallowed a giggle. She wanted to say, "Oh, I *flew* to school this morning." But one look at Miss Rebecca's face told her that wouldn't be the thing to say. She tried to straighten her bonnet, her kerchief and her skirt all at the same time. "I——" she began.

Fortunately Miss Rebecca had no time to wait for an answer to her question. "Oh dear," she said, " 'tis time for the bell," and she began to pull a long rope that hung just inside the door.

"Now go along." Miss Rebecca gave Betsy a little push toward the door. "And see that thee looks a little neater after this," she added.

Betsy wanted to say, "It was all because of the peppermint stick," but she knew Miss Rebecca wouldn't understand. She was sorry she didn't look tidy on her first day at school—but not too sorry. It was nice to think that George wouldn't be quite so lonely with the peppermint stick to keep him company.

IV

THE WAGON RIDE

IT WAS First Day and the Griscom family were walking home from meeting. Usually they walked two by two—Debby and Susan, Mary and Sarah, Hannah and Rachel, Betsy and George. Mr. Griscom carried Martha. Mrs. Griscom carried the baby.

But one day it was different. A young man was walking with Debby. His name was Edwin Bolton.

Edwin walked home with Debby after meeting for two months. Then he began to call on her in the middle of the week. Before long he was having dinner with the Griscom family after meeting. By summer all the children thought of him as a member of the family.

Betsy was especially fond of Edwin. She always ran to meet him when he came. She always begged him to stay when he was ready to leave.

49

The Griscom family were walking home from meeting.

Then, one day, Betsy ran up the stairs to George's room. George, who was playing on the floor, looked up and smiled. "Betsy," he began, "I——"

"Sh!" Betsy put a finger to her lips. Then she closed the door quietly behind her.

George looked puzzled. "What's the matter, Betsy?" he whispered. "Why did thee do that?"

Betsy looked very serious. "George, I was walking through the hall just now, and I heard Mother and Father talking. Something terrible is going to happen."

"Something terrible?" George looked at Betsy. She did look pale. He began to feel frightened. "What's going to happen?" he asked.

Betsy sat down beside George and folded her arms. "It's Edwin," she said. "Does thee know what Edwin is going to do? He's going to marry Debby and take her away. Debby isn't going to live with us any more. She's going to another house—with Edwin."

Debby? George looked puzzled. Debby was like a second mother to him. She had helped take care of him when he was little. He couldn't imagine their house without Debby. "Oh, Betsy," he said, shaking his head. "That *is* terrible."

"Well!" Betsy stood up and stamped her foot. "I've always liked Edwin. I thought he was nice. But if he's going to take Debby away——" Tears came to her eyes. "If he's going to take Debby away I'm never going to speak to him again, or go anywhere with him or . . . or anything!"

George looked at Betsy. He remembered how Edwin had brought popcorn on cold winter evenings and helped them pop it in the fireplace. He had brought them peaches, too, from his father's farm. He had shown them where to find wild strawberries in the summer.

But if Edwin was taking Debby away—— George stamped his foot, too. "I won't either," he said.

"When he comes this afternoon," Betsy said firmly, "I'm not even going downstairs."

George stomped around the room. "I'm not either," he declared.

A few minutes later Betsy and George heard the front door open. Then a deep voice called out, "Good afternoon, everyone!"

"It's Edwin." Betsy closed her lips tight. "Let's be real quiet," she whispered. "If he doesn't hear anyone maybe he'll go away."

But suddenly the house was filled with voices. Everyone had come into the living room to talk to Edwin. Betsy could hear her father's voice above the others. She couldn't tell what he was saying, but he sounded pleased and happy.

"Humph!" Betsy tossed her head. "They can talk to him if they want to," she said. "I'm not going down."

"I'm not either." George shook his head, but he looked a little doubtful. It was always fun when Edwin came to the house. And he wondered why everyone sounded so excited.

At that moment the door to his room opened and Hannah looked in. "Come on downstairs,"

The door opened and Hannah looked in.

she said. "Edwin has brought his father's wagon. He's taking us all for a ride. Even Mother and Father are going."

George looked at Betsy. He had never ridden in a wagon. He knew she hadn't either. "Let's go, Betsy——" he began.

But Betsy was staring straight ahead as if she couldn't see either George or Hannah. "We're not going," she said.

"Not going?" Hannah stared at her in surprise. "Betsy Griscom," she said, "whatever is the matter?"

"Nothing." Betsy tossed her head. "But George and I aren't going."

Hannah disappeared, but a few minutes later she was back again. "I don't know why the two of thee are acting like this," she said, "but Mother says she won't go unless both of thee go, too."

Betsy looked at George and George looked

❀❀❀

at Betsy. "Well——" Betsy didn't know what
to do. She thought how hard her mother worked
day after day. Her mother went to meeting on
First Day and to market once a week. Outside
of that she seldom left the house. Suddenly Betsy
knew that she couldn't keep her mother from
going on this ride to the country. "All right,"
she said. "We'll go, won't we, George?"

"Of course." George had wanted to go from
the very beginning. He raced down the stairs
two steps at a time.

It was fun in the big wagon. Mr. and Mrs.
Griscom and Edwin sat up in front on the high
wooden seat. The rest of the family sat on the
deep bed of hay which Edwin had spread in the
bottom of the wagon. Everyone laughed and
talked—everyone except Betsy.

Betsy liked riding in the big wagon. She liked
feeling the cool wind blow through her hair. She

liked seeing roads and houses she had never seen before. But every time she looked at Debby she felt like crying. "Debby can't leave us," she whispered to herself. "She just can't."

They drove for a long time. When the sun began to set they were far out in the country. Then Edwin called back over his shoulder, "I'm going to show all of thee a house." He looked very pleased and happy. "It's a very special house."

Everyone started to whisper and smile. They all seemed to know that this very special house was going to be Debby's and Edwin's home after they were married.

Betsy looked at her older sisters. How could they be so happy when they knew Debby was going to leave them?

Betsy put her head down on her arm. Everyone thought she was asleep, so no one bothered her.

But she wasn't asleep. She was thinking hard. And the more she thought about Debby's new home the more unhappy she became.

They had been driving all afternoon. That meant Debby's and Edwin's house would be far away from their own house on Mulberry Street. "It will be much too far to walk," Betsy whispered to herself. "We'll be able to visit Debby only when Edwin can borrow his father's wagon." Betsy knew a busy farmer wouldn't be able to lend his wagon very often. "And the winters!" Betsy thought. "Sometimes the roads are so covered with snow, they can't be used for months and months. We'll never get to see Debby then."

Betsy kept her head buried in her arms. She knew if she looked up she would begin to cry. Unhappy as she was, she didn't want to spoil the afternoon for everyone else.

They rode on and on. It seemed to Betsy they

would never stop. But finally she heard Edwin's loud "Whoa!" and raised her head.

It was almost dark and Betsy couldn't see much. But even in the dim light she could see that they weren't in the country anymore.

Betsy blinked and looked about her carefully. She had never been outside Philadelphia before. She wanted to see everything in this strange town so far away from home.

She blinked again. There seemed to be something familiar about this street. The houses looked like houses she had seen before. She began to wonder if all towns looked the same as Philadelphia.

Then she saw little Janey Adams walking down the street. Janey lived next door to the Griscoms', not in a strange city. Janey would be in Philadelphia and she would surely be on Mulberry Street.

It *was* Mulberry Street! Suddenly all the

houses looked familiar. They weren't far from home.

"Everyone out!" Edwin jumped down and held out his hands. One by one, the Griscoms jumped out of the wagon.

"Well, here it is." Edwin looked at Debby and smiled. "Does thee like it?"

Everyone looked at the house except Betsy. She looked down the street at their own house not far away.

"You see," Edwin went on, "I thought it would be nice for Debby to be close to all of thee. If we live here thee can come to visit her as often as thee like."

Betsy still hadn't looked at the house, but she ran up to Edwin and grabbed his arm. "Oh, Edwin," she cried, "I think it's the most beautiful house in all the world."

Everyone laughed, and suddenly Betsy felt very happy. Debby was going to be close to them after all. And Edwin would be her brother-in-law! "Almost like George," Betsy said to herself.

Betsy went up to her brother. "I suppose," she whispered, "we *do* need a few more boys in the family."

George looked around at his nine sisters. "I'll say we do," he said. "I hadn't thought of it *that* way." Then he looked at Betsy and smiled. "Did thee like the wagon ride?" he asked.

"I . . ." Betsy looked serious for a minute. "I *didn't* like it," she said softly, "but I like it now. Oh, George." She laughed. "I think it was a wonderful ride."

By the time Betsy's eighth birthday had passed, Edwin and Debby were married and living in their own house down the street. And everyone was very happy about it—especially Betsy and George.

V

THE VISIT

"**B**ETSY!"

    "Yes?"

"Can thee see anything?"

"No."

"I can't either. Does thee think he is in there?"

"I don't know. 'Tis as dark as pitch. I can't see a thing."

Betsy and George stood on tiptoe. Their noses were pressed hard against a window. Above their heads was an old sign with the words "Benj. FRANKLIN, Printer & Bookshop."

"Well!" Betsy turned away from the window. She put on her bonnet and began to tie the strings under her chin. "It's no use, George. We might as well go home. We can't see a thing."

"But I did so want to see him. Let's wait a

little while longer, Betsy. Perhaps he'll come out."

They were so busy talking they didn't hear the door open. They didn't see a face look out.

"Good afternoon!"

"Oh!" Betsy and George were frightened by the unexpected greeting. They both jumped back, startled. "Oh!"

"You wanted something?" The tone was low and friendly. There was a smile on the man's round face.

Betsy and George looked at each other. They had wanted, more than anything else, a little glimpse of Dr. Franklin. Now that they saw him face to face they didn't know what to say.

"Oh!" Betsy felt that it was up to her to say something. "Well . . ." She stopped again. How could she tell a famous man that she and George just wanted to look at him for a few minutes? Her face grew red.

Betsy and George met Dr. Franklin face to face.

64

Dr. Franklin seemed to guess what she was thinking. He opened the door a little wider. He motioned for them to come in.

One minute Betsy and George were on the street in the bright sunlight. The next minute they found themselves inside the printing shop.

It was cool and damp inside. There was the unfamiliar smell of ink. Betsy looked around her. She had never been in a printing shop before.

"This is very nice. I like having visitors." Dr. Franklin pulled out two high stools. "Sit down and tell me about yourselves." He looked over his spectacles at Betsy. "First, now, tell me your names."

Betsy folded her hands on her lap. She sat up very straight. She looked as if she were answering a question in school. "My name is Elizabeth Griscom," she said, "but everyone calls me Betsy. This is my brother George."

Betsy and George sat on high stools.

"Griscom?" Dr. Franklin repeated the name. "Could you be Samuel Griscom's children?"

"Yes, sir. We are."

"The Griscom family is an old one in Philadelphia."

Betsy looked pleased. "Yes, sir, it is. My great-grandfather came to America in 1681. Even before Mr. William Penn came over from England."

"My, that was a long time ago. You're a real dyed-in-the-wool American, Betsy." Dr. Franklin bent down and looked at her closely. "Now let me see if I can guess how old you are." He pulled at his chin for a few minutes. "I'd say—— I'd say about nine years old."

"That's right." Betsy smiled. "I was born on the first day of the week, the first day of the month, and the first day of the year, in 1752."

At that moment the big bell which hung in the State House belfry began to ring, and its deep, low tones filled the room. The type rattled. The windows clattered. Even the pewter cups on the shelf danced up and down in time to its ringing.

When it finally stopped, Betsy began to laugh.

"I know something else that happened in 1752," she said. "That was the year the big bell in the State House came over from England."

"That's right." Dr. Franklin smiled at her. "I had forgotten that. I was there on the dock the day it arrived. I even followed it all the way up the street to the State House lawn."

"I did, too!"

"You?"

"Yes." Betsy laughed. "You see, Father helped build the State House belfry. So the whole family was excited when the big bell finally came. I was just a baby, but Mother took me anyway. She held me up high so I could see it. She says everyone was pleased when the first note rang out. It was so clear and loud. But then the second note——"

Dr. Franklin nodded. "I'll never forget that second note," he said. "It was so dull and flat we couldn't believe our ears. We couldn't believe our eyes, either! The very first note had made a great crack down one side."

"I would have sent it right back to England," said George.

"That is what a great many people wanted to do," Dr. Franklin answered. "But the captain refused to take it back. You know, the bell weighs two thousand pounds. He said he wouldn't have room for it and his new cargo, too.

"Finally a foundry near Philadelphia said they would try to recast it," Dr. Franklin went on. "They took the old bell and made a mold. Then they broke the bell into small pieces and melted them. After that they poured the metal back into the mold."

"Was it a good bell?" George looked up eagerly.

Dr. Franklin shook his head. "It was a terrible bell. It sounded as bad as the old one after it was cracked. It went *bung! bung! bung!* It sounded as if someone was pounding on a big, old kettle. People put their hands over their ears every time it rang."

George laughed. It was funny to think of all the people in Philadelphia standing with their hands over their heads every time the bell rang. "It doesn't sound like that now," he said. "What happened?"

"The foundry decided to try again," Dr. Franklin answered. "You see, this was the first large bell ever made in America. All of us wanted to be proud of it. But it is very difficult to learn how to make a good bell. It was a long time before they found the right recipe."

"The right recipe?" Betsy laughed. "Do they need a recipe to make a bell?"

"Of course they need a recipe to make a bell," Dr. Franklin said. "Bell metal is made of copper and tin and bronze. They have to use just the right amount of each to get a strong bell with a good tone."

He looked at Betsy. "If you used two cups of baking powder and one teaspoon of flour you wouldn't have very good biscuits, would you?"

Betsy threw back her head and laughed. "They'd rise so high in the oven they'd pop the door wide open," she said.

Dr. Franklin nodded. "Well, that's the way it is with bells—they need to be made of exact amounts of ingredients. The bellmakers tried so much of this and so much of that and a little bit of the other."

He looked at Betsy again. "Does your mother ever bake one cooky first before she bakes the whole batch, just to see if the recipe is right?"

"Oh, yes." Betsy nodded. "She always does."

"Well," Dr. Franklin went on, "that's what the bellmakers did. They made little bells and tried them first."

Betsy and George looked at each other and laughed. It was funny to think of men making little bells and then ringing them to see if they were right.

"I wish I'd been there," said Betsy.

"I do, too," George said.

"I do, too," said Dr. Franklin. "It must have been a big day when they finally made one that was just right. Then, you see, they took that same recipe and cast the big bell again. This time the tone was good. And so far," he added, smiling, "it hasn't cracked. Now tell me this! Do you know what is written on the bell?"

"Oh, yes." Betsy didn't hesitate for a minute. "It says: 'Proclaim liberty throughout all the land unto all the inhabitants thereof.' It's from the Bible," she added.

"Why, that's fine." Dr. Franklin looked very pleased. "I'm glad you know what it says. Every time I hear it ring I think it is saying, 'Liberty!

Liberty! Liberty!' because that's what the people who made it wanted it to say."

Dr. Franklin looked out the shop window for a few minutes. "Philadelphia is full of bells," he said. "Some say, 'Come to church.' Some say, 'Time for work.' Some say, 'Hurry to school.' The big bell on the rocks out in the harbor cries, 'Danger!' The night watchman's bell says, 'All is well!' Some bells cry, 'Fire!' Some bells strike the hour. The market bells say, 'Come and buy.'

"But my favorite bell is the State House bell. It says, 'Liberty!' every time it rings. It is right that here in America its voice should be louder than all the other bells put together."

He looked at Betsy and his eyes twinkled. "I'm glad you and the 'Liberty' bell are twins. It's a nice kind of twin to have."

Betsy felt happy. How nice of Dr. Franklin to have called the bell her twin!

Betsy could have stayed there all afternoon

talking to Dr. Franklin. But she knew she shouldn't stay too long. "We must go now," she said, slipping off the high stool. "Thee has been very kind, Dr. Franklin. Thank thee very much for a pleasant afternoon. George and I will never forget this visit with thee."

Dr. Franklin walked to the door with them and waved as they hurried off.

It wasn't far from Dr. Franklin's printing shop on Second and Race streets to the Griscom house on Mulberry Street. Betsy and George ran all the way.

"I do hope Mother won't think we were rude," said Betsy, running even faster. "And I hope I'm not too late. This was my night to help cook supper."

"And I have to get water from the well and fill the wood box," said George.

Finally they were home. They ran up the steps and lifted the latch.

Betsy hurried to the kitchen. Without a word she took down a large, white apron and tied it around her waist. George grabbed the water bucket and started for the well.

They both knew there would be no time to talk until all the chores were finished. Their story of the afternoon's visit would have to wait.

Betsy didn't mind waiting. She was rather glad she could keep this bit of news as her own secret for a little while. It seemed to make it last longer. And that was very important.

Betsy's visit with Dr. Franklin had seemed like a real adventure to her. She didn't know when anything half so exciting would ever happen to her again.

"Waste not, want not," was the household motto. Everything had to be used sparingly and carefully—food, clothing, water, wood—even a story. Betsy knew that this one small adventure would last for many a long winter evening.

VI

THE NEW SCHOOL

WHEN BETSY was ten she felt very grown-up. She was too old for Miss Rebecca's school. Now she could go to the Friends' School on South Fourth Street.

Betsy had been very eager to go to this large public grammar school. She had counted the months, the weeks and the days. Now, at last, she was on her way to school with her older sisters.

When they reached the schoolyard Betsy's sisters ran off to see their old friends. They were so excited about being back in school, they forgot for a few minutes that this was Betsy's first day.

Betsy looked at the boys and girls who hurried past her. Many of them weren't Quakers. They were different from her old friends and very grown-up. Everything was different. Betsy had thought the big school would be exciting. Instead she felt lonely and very small. Tears came to her eyes.

At that moment Betsy's oldest sister, Sarah, came back to look for her. "Betsy Griscom," she said, "thee looks ready to cry. What ails thee, child?"

"I don't like it here." Betsy brushed the tears from her eyes. "I wish I could go back to Miss Rebecca's school. I want my old friends. They're like us. They're all Quakers."

"Fie!" Sarah took her little sister's hand. "Thee will make new friends fast enough. After all, this is a Quaker school. Boys and girls who aren't Quakers come here from all over Philadelphia. Some of them are very wealthy. They could go anywhere. But they choose this school. Isn't thee glad the Quakers run such a good school?"

Betsy nodded her head. "But they seem so different," she said. "So grown-up."

Sarah laughed. "Thee will grow up, too, Betsy. It will not take long."

Sarah was right. Betsy did grow up fast during that year. Before long she had made many new friends. She soon found that it didn't make any difference at all whether they were Quakers.

And her friends found out in no time that Betsy was as gay and friendly as she was pretty. Her white Quaker bonnet didn't hide her bright-blue eyes or her curly hair.

School started at eight o'clock in the morning. For two hours there were reading and writing and arithmetic. Then the teacher would tap on his desk with a ruler. "Ten o'clock," he would say. "Now is the time for each pupil to work at that art or trade she most delights in."

"Most delights in." Betsy always repeated these words to herself. They were wonderful words. Betsy knew very well what art or trade she most delighted in. There was no doubt about it. Betsy Griscom "most delighted in" sewing—and now she could sew.

Betsy sat with her head bent over her work.

For two wonderful hours every morning Betsy sat with her head bent over her work. Why were the two hours from eight to ten so long?

Why were the two hours from ten to twelve so short?

At twelve o'clock all the pupils went home to eat. Then at two they were back in school again. Once more, from two until four, there were reading, writing and arithmetic. Then at four o'clock the ruler tapped again. And once more there were those wonderful words: "Now is the time for each pupil to do that art or trade she most delights in."

And once more, for two wonderful hours, Betsy could work on her sewing. Then at six o'clock it was time to go home.

One evening Betsy and her friend Susannah Claypoole were walking home from school. It was late in December and quite dark at six o'clock. At the corner of the street the lamp-lighter was at work.

Susannah kicked a rock with the toe of her shoe. "I'm tired of school," she said. "Aren't you, Betsy? It's dark when we leave home in the mornings. It's dark when we come home in the evenings. We even have to go on Saturday mornings. We never have time to do anything else."

Betsy looked down at the big carpetbag she was carrying. "Oh, I don't mind!" she said. "The time seems to pass quickly. I almost finished my quilt today."

"Oh, you!" Susannah laughed. "As long as you can sew you don't care about anything else. Don't you ever get tired of sewing, Betsy? Don't you ever want to knit or weave for a change?"

Betsy shook her head. "I like to sew best," she said.

"I suppose you like to sew because you sew so well," Susannah went on.

"Or maybe I sew well because I like it," Betsy answered.

Susannah stopped in the middle of the sidewalk. "I never thought of that before. Do we do things well because we like to do them, or do we like to do them because we do them well?"

Betsy laughed. "I don't know. Perhaps 'tis a little bit of each."

Susannah looked at Betsy. "Anyway, you're lucky. You're lucky because you like to do what you do well, and you do well what you like to do. You're lucky, too, because you're pretty. Everyone says you're the prettiest girl in school."

Betsy's cheeks turned red. "Oh, that isn't true!" she cried. "Thee is pretty, too. Thee should be very glad thee is thee."

Susannah laughed. "I am glad I'm me. And I'm glad you're you. But most of all I'm glad we're friends."

"I am, too." Betsy smiled. "Thee is my very best friend, Susannah. I'm so glad we go to the same school."

VII

SOMETHING EXCITING CAN HAPPEN!

Betsy liked school, but she liked the long summer months better. "Isn't it wonderful?" she said as she and Susannah walked down the street together. "No lessons for three whole months!"

"What shall we do?" said Susannah. "Let's do something special to celebrate our vacation."

"I know," Betsy said. "Let's go down to the pier."

Susannah wrinkled her nose. "You *always* want to go to the pier. I'd like to go somewhere else for a change."

"But 'tis so exciting down there," Betsy said. "Something's always happening. It's not the same place really, because it changes every day.

There are always new boats and new people and new cargoes."

"And new smells." Susannah wrinkled her nose again.

"Oh, I like the smells," Betsy said. "I like the smell of tar and turpentine and paint and spices."

"All right, I'll go with you this time. But I'll tell you right now, I'm not going down to that pier every day. So there!"

"Oh, I wouldn't want thee to." Betsy pretended to be shocked. "I wouldn't think of going more than every *other* day."

"Not every other day either." Susannah laughed in spite of herself. "I don't know why I always give in to you, Betsy. I suppose I'll end up spending half the summer down there with you."

Susannah was silent for a minute, looking at the sky. "It's going to rain. I really don't think we should go today."

"But this is the first day we've had even a tiny bit of sunshine for ever so long," Betsy said. "Let's go anyway." She untied her bonnet strings. " 'Tis warm and it wouldn't be too terrible if it did rain. I won't melt, Sue, and neither will thee."

Betsy looked up and sniffed the air. " 'Tis an exciting day, with the wind and the dark clouds and the sun breaking through. Perhaps something exciting will happen."

Susannah laughed. "You always think something exciting is going to happen but it never does. Don't you know by now that nothing exciting ever happens to us?"

"But it *could*," Betsy said. "Exciting things happen to all kinds of people."

"And exciting things *don't* happen to a lot of people, too," said Susannah.

Betsy laughed. They had almost reached the river now. She could smell the water and hear the gentle lapping of the waves against the old wooden pier.

"Sue!" Betsy grabbed Susannah's hand. "Look! We're in luck. There's a big ship in the harbor—a really big one—from England."

"How do you know it's from England?" Susannah asked. "You can see only the top of the mast from here."

"I can see the flag," Betsy said.

"Well, maybe you can tell what country a ship is from by its flag," said Susannah, "but I can't."

"Susannah Claypoole!" Betsy stopped in the middle of the path and stared at Susannah. "Thee doesn't mean to tell me that all flags *really* look alike to thee."

"Oh, no, of course not," Susannah said. "I know they have different colors and different designs. But I don't know which flag belongs to which country."

Betsy laughed. "Each design means something. It tells something important that's happened to a country—something to remember. Why, a flag is like a page out of a history book, flying in the breeze."

They were close to the big ship now. Betsy and Susannah sat down on the pier to watch. The gangplank had just been lowered. There was a great deal of noise and confusion. Sailors rushed back and forth shouting to one another. Passengers walked slowly as if afraid of the solid ground.

"They still have their sea legs," said Betsy, laughing. "They're so used to walking on the rolling deck, they don't know how to walk on flat ground any more."

The girls were too busy watching the ship to notice that someone was standing beside them.

"Good day!"

Betsy and Susannah looked up. A boy was

Betsy and Susannah were close to the

big ship. There were noise and confusion.

standing beside Betsy. He took off his cap and smiled at them.

Betsy and Susannah looked down so their bonnets hid their faces. They weren't supposed to talk to strange boys. They pretended they hadn't seen him.

"Ahem!" The boy twirled his cap on the end of his finger. "Ahem!"

Betsy and Susannah looked up but they stared straight at the ship. As far as they were concerned the boy might have been a log on the pier or a piece of rope.

He was certainly as quiet as a log or a piece of rope. Time and time again Betsy thought he had gone away. But when she tilted her bonnet and glanced to her right he was still there. Every time she looked at him he smiled and twirled his cap. But Betsy always looked away quickly, as if she hadn't seen him.

Suddenly the sun disappeared. The clouds

became darker and the wind stronger. Susannah looked up at the sky. "We'd best go," she said.

A sudden gust of wind swept up from the river. Before Betsy could grab her bonnet it was off her head and skimming along toward the water.

"I'll get it." The boy scampered over rocks and driftwood. His coattails flew out behind him.

The bonnet and the boy disappeared behind a large rock. "He'll never catch it," Betsy said. "We might as well go home."

But as they turned to walk away they saw the boy running toward them. He was twirling the bonnet over his head.

" 'Twill be no good by the time he gets it here," Betsy said. "It might as well have gone into the river."

But the bonnet looked surprisingly fresh when the boy handed it to her a few minutes later.

"Thank thee." Betsy reached for the bonnet. "Thank thee very much."

"My name's Joe Ashburn." The boy held onto the bonnet strings. "I've seen you down here lots of times. You must like ships," he said. "Do you?"

"She certainly does." Susannah laughed. "I think she would live on a ship if she could."

"Really?" Joe looked at Betsy and smiled. "I'm going to live on one someday," he said. "My uncle owns three big ships. I'm going to sea on one of them just as soon as I finish school."

Betsy forgot she wasn't supposed to talk to strange boys. "I think I'd be a sailor, too, if I were a boy," she said. "But girls can't be sailors. I'll probably never even get on a boat."

"Haven't you ever been on a big ship?" Joe looked as if he couldn't believe her.

Betsy shook her head.

"Would you like to go on one?" he asked.

"Like to?" Betsy's eyes were sparkling. "Indeed I would."

"Right now?" Joe said. He nodded toward the river. "The captain of that big ship is a good friend of my uncle's. He's going to be at our house for dinner tomorrow. I'm sure he'd let me take you aboard if I asked him. I've been on lots of other times the ship was in port."

"Oh, I couldn't," Betsy said, startled.

"Why not?" Joe looked puzzled.

"Sue and I couldn't go alone," she answered. "Our mothers wouldn't like it."

Joe laughed. "But you won't be alone," he said. "I'll be with you and——" He stopped. "But who *are* you? I should tell the captain."

"See," said Betsy, "thee does not even know our names. We couldn't possibly go with thee."

Joe laughed again. "That's no excuse. I imagine you could tell me your names if you tried real hard."

Betsy couldn't keep from smiling. "All right," she said. "My name is Betsy Griscom and this is Susannah Claypoole. But we still can't go with thee."

"Why not?" Joe asked again. "The ship will be here for weeks unloading and loading again. It isn't going to sail away with you aboard."

"Oh, I know that!" Betsy tossed her head. "It's just——"

"Walking around up there will be just as safe as walking around here on the pier," Joe said. "Nothing could happen to you. And I'll show you all over the ship," he went on eagerly. "Come on. It'll be fun."

Joe pointed up to the deck. "Look! Wouldn't you like to stand 'way up there? The ship rocks back and forth. If you look down the river it's almost like being out on the ocean."

"Come on, Sue." Betsy tied the strings of her bonnet under her chin. "This may be the only chance we'll ever have to go on a big ship like that. I'll go if thee will."

Joe didn't wait for Susannah's answer. "You two stay here for a few minutes. I'll go up and talk to the captain. I won't be long."

He was off before the girls could say anything. They watched him as he ran across the pier, down the steps and out toward the gangplank.

When he got to the gangplank he stopped and looked from side to side. Suddenly he hid behind a stack of barrels.

"Well!" Susannah put her hands on her hips and pressed her lips together. "Now what do you think he's doing?" she asked. "That's a strange way to act, I must say!"

Betsy shook her head. "I can't imagine," she said slowly. "Why would he want to hide?"

As they watched they saw Joe peep out from behind one of the barrels and look from side to

side. Then, quick as a lizard, he darted out from
his hiding place and scurried up the gangplank.

Betsy and Susannah were too surprised to say
anything. They began to walk slowly across the
pier, down the steps and out toward the ship.
Their eyes were on Joe every minute.

"Look! He's hiding again!" Susannah
pointed toward the deck.

Betsy shrugged her shoulders. Susannah was
right. She could just see Joe's head sticking over
the top of a large coil of rope.

Betsy felt angry and disappointed and puzzled, but she couldn't keep from giggling. " 'Tis
a queer way to visit the captain," she said.

"Captain, my eye!" Susannah said. "I don't
think he knows the captain. I don't think the
captain's coming to his house for dinner tomorrow. I don't think his uncle has three ships.
He probably doesn't even *have* an uncle."

Betsy giggled again. It was all so silly. Still

she *was* disappointed. It would have been fun to go on the ship and look around. "Why did he tell us all that if it wasn't true?" she asked.

"Boys!" said Susannah, as if that explained everything. "He thought you were pretty, Betsy Griscom, and he wanted you to think he was important. Next time he sees us down here he'll probably have some wonderful excuse and expect us to believe it."

Betsy nodded. "I suppose thee is right, Sue. We might as well go home." They turned and started to walk away.

"Wait! Wait!"

They turned around. There behind them was Joe, running as fast as he could. "Wait for me!"

The girls stopped. "I wonder what he's going to tell us this time," Susannah said.

"Whew!" Joe sat down on a rock and tried to catch his breath. "I thought you'd gone," he said, gasping. "I couldn't find you."

Susannah put her hands on her hips. "I don't know about you, Master Joe Ashburn, but we've no desire to hide behind barrels and coils of rope when we go aboard a ship."

"Oh, that!" Joe laughed. "You won't have to hide."

"Then why did thee?" Betsy asked.

"Well, you see," Joe explained, "I don't know this crew. If I had told them I know the captain, they would have laughed at me. They would have thought I was just making it up. They would never have let me on the ship. So I had to sneak on when no one was looking."

Betsy and Susannah looked at each other. Was Joe really telling the truth? It was hard to know what to believe.

"Come on." Joe took each girl by the arm. "See the captain up there on the deck? Look, he sees us. He's waving."

The girls looked up. It was the captain. His

gold braid glittered in the sunlight. And he was certainly waving. Was he waving to them?

"Come on." Joe led them toward the ship. "The captain is a busy man. We mustn't keep him waiting."

A few minutes later they reached the top of the gangplank. They could see then that the captain was waving to them.

Joe was as good as his word. He took the girls from one end of the ship to the other. He told them the names of the different sails and how they were used. He took them up to the bridge and into the captain's quarters. He explained everything.

Finally he took them to the bow of the ship. "Now!" He looked at Betsy and smiled. "Close your eyes and take a deep breath."

The wind was rising higher every minute. Dark clouds raced across the sky. The sun appeared and then disappeared again. As Betsy

The wind blew through Betsy's hair.

closed her eyes the big ship rolled from side to side.

"Oh!" Betsy opened her eyes and threw back her head. The wind blew through her hair and whipped at her skirts. The gathering storm made everything much more exciting. "It *is* like being in the middle of the ocean," she said. "I feel as if I'm sailing to England—to India— clear around the world! Oh, Joe, 'tis wonderful. 'Tis the most exciting thing I've ever done."

A few drops of rain began to fall. Soon the drizzle was turning into a downpour. The ship tossed and turned.

Betsy smiled at Joe. " 'Tis like a real storm at sea."

Susannah ran for cover, and in a few minutes Betsy and Joe followed her.

Betsy tilted her head until she could see the flag at the very top of the ship. The wind had stretched it straight. There wasn't a fold or a ripple. "The flag looks as if it were pasted on the sky," she said. "It's so smooth and straight. And so bright," she added. "Look how it shines through the rain."

A moment later the captain came up to them. "I have a problem," he said. "Perhaps you would help me?"

"Yes, sir." Joe stood at attention. "Anything at all, sir."

"There's a young girl on this ship," the captain began, "who came with her maid from England. Her name is Mary Allen. Her parents died last year and she has come to America to live with her uncle. He lives in Baltimore and was supposed to be here to meet her when the ship landed."

The captain unfolded a slip of paper he had been holding in his hand. "A few minutes ago," he went on, "a messenger gave me this letter. Mary's uncle left Baltimore three days ago,

but heavy rains washed out the roads and he has
been delayed. He asked me to take Mary to the
inn and place her in the care of Mrs. Baker, the
innkeeper's wife."

The captain frowned. "Everything has gone
wrong," he said. "Mary's maid is ill and they
should get to the inn as soon as possible. However, I can't leave the ship now—some very valu-
able cargo is being unloaded. I'd appreciate it
if the three of you would see Mary and her maid
to the inn. I'm sure if you go with her she will
be in good hands."

VIII

SOVEREIGN FOR A SEAMSTRESS

HALF AN hour later a carriage stopped in front of the inn. Joe got out first, then helped Betsy and Susannah. Just as Mary started to step out, the horses lurched. At that same moment there was a loud ripping sound. Mary's full skirt had caught in one of the wheels.

"Oh, dear!" Mary tried to brush her torn, mud-splattered skirt. " 'Twas the last clean dress I had. We were on the ocean for two months. Water was very scarce and we couldn't wash our clothes. I saved this dress so I'd look nice when I met my uncle. Now look at it!"

"Oh, I'm so sorry, Miss Mary!" The maid leaned back against the carriage seat and closed her eyes. "Here I am ill and not able to do a thing to help you."

Mary looked at her torn, mud-spattered skirt.

Betsy thought the maid looked even paler than when they had left the ship.

"Don't worry about that." Mary looked down at her dress. "You wouldn't be able to fix this anyway. It's too badly torn."

The dress did seem to be completely ruined, but Betsy looked at it carefully. "It can be fixed," she said finally. "I'll fix it for thee."

"I don't see how," Mary said. "Look, the whole side is torn."

Susannah patted Mary's arm. "If Betsy says she can fix it, she can. Don't you worry. She may be only eleven years old, but she can sew as well as her mother."

"Hush!" Betsy put her hand over Susannah's mouth and laughed. "Don't listen to her," she said. "But I can fix thy dress for thee. I'm sure I can."

An hour later Mary was standing on top of a stool. Betsy walked slowly around her. She pinned tucks and straightened the hem until the front of Mary's dress looked like a pincushion.

"Now." Betsy picked up the needle and thread and thimble Mary had taken from her trunk. She began to take big stitches where the pins were. "Turn slowly, Mary. This won't take long."

Mary looked down at her gratefully. "This is almost like making a new dress," she said. "Really harder, because the material was torn. You're a wonderful seamstress, Betsy."

Betsy laughed. " 'Tis fun," she said. "Thy dress is beautiful, Mary. The material is lovely. It feels good in my hands."

Betsy worked on the dress all afternoon. She replaced the big stitches with tiny, even ones. Finally every ruffle and flounce was back in place. The tucks and the hem were straight again. The dried mud had been brushed off. It did, indeed, look like a new dress.

By late afternoon the storm had cleared and the sun was shining brightly. "Thy uncle will surely come soon," Betsy said as she told Mary good-by. "It won't take long for the roads to dry this time of the year."

"I hope so." Mary looked lonely standing at the inn door. "Will you come back in the morning?" she asked. "Even if he does come we won't leave right away. I want you to meet him."

Betsy was pleased by the invitation. She felt as if she and Mary were old friends. "I'll see thee tomorrow."

It was about ten o'clock when Betsy got to the inn the next morning. She knew without asking that Mary's uncle had come—Mary was waiting for her outside with a big smile.

"He's here," Mary called as soon as Betsy was close enough to hear her. "He came in early this morning."

A tall man came to the doorway. Betsy almost gasped. "Mary's uncle must be a very rich man," she thought. Every curl of his white powdered wig was in place. He had silver buckles on his shoes and his purple coat was made of satin. His shirt had row upon row of ruffles. His cane had a golden head. "No wonder Mary wanted to look her best when she met him."

His smile was as friendly as Mary's. "Well! Well! I've been hearing a great deal about you, young lady. I don't know what my niece would have done without your help. I wanted to leave right away for Baltimore, but she wouldn't go without telling you good-by."

Betsy curtsied. " 'Twas nothing," she said. "It was a pleasure to help her."

Mary's uncle looked toward a large carriage that was standing in the street. Betsy noticed that it was already loaded with Mary's baggage. The coachman held the reins in his hands. Mary's maid was already inside.

"Good-by." Mary held out both hands to Betsy. "Perhaps we'll meet again someday. And thank you again for all you did. I can never tell you how much it meant to me."

They stepped into the carriage. The footman closed the door. Then they were off.

Betsy stood still and watched the big carriage roll down the street. She waved, and Mary's white handkerchief waved back to her until handkerchief, carriage and horses were all out of sight.

Betsy started walking slowly down the street. But before she had gone very far, she heard someone calling to her.

"Wait, Miss Betsy! Wait!" Betsy saw the innkeeper running toward her and waving his hands. She stopped and waited for him. She couldn't imagine why Mr. Baker would want to talk to her.

"Miss Betsy!" Mr. Baker was puffing and panting when he stopped beside her. He was a fat man and not used to running. "Miss Betsy—" he tried to catch his breath—"the gentleman who was here with his niece left this with me."

"Wait, Miss Betsy!" the innkeeper shouted.

He opened his hand and there in his palm lay
four shillings and one sovereign. "Two of the

shillings are for Miss Susannah," he said, "and the other two are for Master Joe."

He looked at Betsy and smiled. "The gentleman said the sovereign was for the little seamstress."

Betsy stared at the money. It looked like a small treasure there in the innkeeper's hand. She couldn't believe her eyes.

"Oh, no," she said, "I couldn't take it!"

"But it's yours," Mr. Baker said. "It certainly isn't mine. Here." He opened Betsy's hand and put the money in it. "Now along with you. I can't stand here all day dilly-dallying and letting my dinner burn black in the oven. Just be glad you were blessed with nimble fingers."

Betsy didn't know whether to laugh or cry. She felt like doing a bit of each. A whole sovereign! That was a great deal of money. She closed her right hand tightly and put her left one over it. She had never had so much money in her hands before. She could hardly believe it.

When Betsy was almost home she saw Susannah coming toward her down the street. "Sue!" Betsy had never been so glad to see her before. All the way home she had been bursting with her news. Now, at last, she could give Susannah her share and tell her the whole story.

Susannah's eyes grew round. She looked gratefully at her own two shillings. Then she looked unbelievingly at Betsy's sovereign. "Oh, Betsy," she cried, "isn't it wonderful!"

Betsy nodded. "I still can't quite believe it," she said. "And won't Joe be surprised? Come on, Sue. I'll run home and tell Mother about the sovereign and put it away. Then thee and I will find Joe and give him his share."

Susannah smiled. "Oh, Betsy," she said, "you were right. Something exciting can happen to anyone." She threw back her head and laughed. "Even to us!"

IX

ICE SKATES IN JULY

BETSY hurried down the street with her sovereign in her hand. Now, at last, she could buy something she had wanted for a long time.

Betsy knew she shouldn't run. Running wasn't proper for a young lady. Besides, it was a very hot day. But she walked faster and faster. Every minute seemed important.

"Skates!" Betsy said the word softly to herself. She was so excited she didn't realize she was talking aloud. "I've always wanted a pair of skates. But skates are expensive," she explained to herself. "I never expected to have a pair. But now . . ."

Betsy turned the sovereign over in her pocket and closed her eyes. She could imagine herself gliding over the ice. "It will be wonderful," she whispered. "Just wonderful." She began to walk even faster.

"Only one more corner." Betsy took off her bonnet and fanned herself. Hurrying along the street in the July sun had made her very warm. She was glad Mr. William's blacksmith shop wasn't any farther.

"Mr. Williams! Mr. Williams!" Betsy shouted. The blacksmith had his back turned toward the doorway. He was hammering on a piece of iron. "Mr. Williams, may I come in?"

"Come in! Come in!" Mr. Williams looked back over his shoulder. "Hello there, Betsy. I'll be through in a minute."

Betsy stepped into the shop and looked around. She was glad the blacksmith was busy. She wanted plenty of time to look at the skates.

Betsy walked around slowly. She had seen skates hanging on the walls of the shop many times. But there was none there now. There

The blacksmith was hammering on a piece of iron.

were horseshoes and harnesses and yokes. There were iron pots and skillets and candle molds. There were cranes and wheels and wagon tongues. There were big locks and keys.

But no skates! Had they all been sold?

At last the hammering stopped and Mr. Williams turned around. "Well, well," he said, wiping his hands on his leather apron. "This is a nice surprise. I've had only three customers so far today. They were all horses badly in need of shoes. 'Tis nice to have a charming customer for a change. What can I do for you?"

Betsy shook her head. "Oh, Mr. Williams," she said, "I'm so disappointed. Thee does not have what I want."

Mr. Williams looked surprised. "I don't have what you want? I have everything a blacksmith shop should have. Everything!"

"Thee does not have skates."

"Skates?" Mr. Williams stared at Betsy. "Did you say skates?" he said very loudly.

Betsy felt as if she had asked for a stick of peppermint candy or a baby bonnet. She didn't know what to say.

"What ails you, child?" Mr. Williams asked.

Betsy shook her head. She felt more bewildered every moment. One *did* buy skates at a blacksmith shop. She was sure of it. Why did Mr. Williams look so surprised?

"Ho, ho! Skates! Skates!" Mr. Williams put his hands to his head and rocked back and forth, laughing.

Now Betsy felt provoked. "But thee does have skates, Mr. Williams," she said. "I've seen them here. I'm sure I have."

Mr. Williams looked at Betsy. "In July?" he asked.

"July?" Betsy stared at the blacksmith. Then she began to laugh, too.

"Oh, my!" he said. He wiped his forehead with his kerchief. "You want to buy skates on a day like this!"

"I didn't think," Betsy said. "I've wanted skates for a long time. Today, when I had the money, I thought about nothing else. I see now 'twas very foolish. I'd best go."

"Go?" Mr. Williams wiped his face again. "I thought you wanted a pair of skates."

"I did." Betsy looked around the shop again. "But thee hasn't any."

Mr. Williams smiled. "Well, I don't have a heap of customers asking for skates in July. But if you want them, you shall have them. I'll see what I have in the loft."

Betsy looked up at a small opening in the ceiling. "Oh, I wouldn't want thee to go up there, Mr. Williams. 'Twould be frightfully hot on a day like this."

Mr. Williams nodded. " 'Twill be hot as four Julys. But I haven't had a good customer in three days. 'Twould be nice to hear a bit of silver tinkling in the drawer again."

He started up the narrow ladder. "Now, I'm not saying those skates won't be melted," he

said as his head disappeared. "Hot enough to
melt anything up here. Don't know why I
bother to keep a fire in my forge."

By this time his feet, too, had disappeared.
Betsy could hear him walking around above her
head. She could hear him moving heavy objects
and opening and closing chests.

At last Betsy saw a foot at the top of the ladder.
Then another foot. Mr. Williams' face was
redder than ever as he looked down at her, but he
was smiling broadly. "These are mighty fine
skates," he said. "They came all the way from
England."

Betsy looked at the blades. They glistened in
the dark shop. "Oh, they're beautiful!" she said.
"They're the most beautiful skates I've ever
seen."

Suddenly Betsy felt frightened. "How much
are they?" she asked.

Mr. Williams pulled at his chin. "Well, as I said, they're mighty fine skates. Don't know when I'll get another pair like them. The price is one sovereign and five shillings."

"Oh!" Betsy put the skates carefully on the counter. She should have known they'd be too expensive.

"On the other hand," Mr. Williams went on, "sometimes we sell winter things a mite cheaper in the summer."

Betsy looked up hopefully.

"But then again I spent a mighty long time in the loft looking for these skates. My time's worth something. I could have finished those horse-shoes by now. Time's money, I always say."

Betsy nodded. Mr. Williams *had* spent a great deal of time in the loft. Her hopes fell again.

The blacksmith continued: "However, some-times skates get a mite rusty during the summer if no one keeps an eye on them. It's a good idea for me to sell them if I can."

Betsy picked up the skates. If they had been made of silver they couldn't have looked more beautiful. "If I had them," she said softly, "I'd make a bag for them and oil them every day."

Mr. Williams smiled. "Every day would be a mite often. Once a month would be about right. Let's say we make the price an even sovereign. You'll never do better than that."

An even sovereign! Betsy couldn't believe that she had heard correctly. The hot July sun and the heat from the forge made her feel a little dizzy.

"One sovereign," Mr. Williams repeated. "What with summer and the rust and not having a good customer for three days. . . . Yes, I'll sell them for a sovereign."

Betsy opened her hand and put the sovereign

on the counter. The skates were hers, really hers. She couldn't believe it.

Betsy could scarcely wait for winter. She had made a little bag for her skates. She oiled them every month as Mr. Williams had said. Now they shone even more brightly than when she had bought them.

Finally it began to grow cold. On the first day of December the river began to freeze. By the end of the week it was hard enough for skating.

The wind howled, but Betsy didn't mind. The snow blew in her face, but she didn't mind that either. The river was frozen and her skates were on her feet.

Betsy skimmed across the ice. "It's like flying. It's like—— Oh!" Betsy bumped into a tall boy who was skating in front of her. "I'm sorry," she said, "but my skates! They go so fast! I'm not used to them. This is the first time I've worn them."

The boy smiled at Betsy. Her cheeks were red and her blue eyes were sparkling. Her curly hair was blowing around her bonnet. "I'm not sorry," he said. "You're Betsy Griscom, aren't you?"

Betsy looked surprised. "How did thee know?" she asked.

The boy twirled around on his skates and then made a deep bow. "I'm John Ross," he said. "I'm a friend of Joe Ashburn. He's told me about you. He's even told me about your skates."

Betsy smiled. "I don't see Joe often, but I've been talking about these skates for months. I'm sure all my friends are tired of hearing about them."

"I don't blame you." John looked down at the skates. "They're beautiful. Can you make a figure eight with them?"

The boy twirled on his skates.

Betsy laughed. "Gracious, no! I've been on
skates only a few times in my whole life. I can't
do anything except bump into people."

"Figure eights aren't hard." John Ross looked
at Betsy and smiled. "I'll teach you. I'm sure it
will be easy for you."

It was easy for Betsy to learn. By the end of the winter John Ross thought she was the best skater in Philadelphia. He thought she was the prettiest girl in Philadelphia, too.

X

"AND ALL IS WELL!"

WINTERS were always long and cold in Philadelphia. There was always a great deal of illness. When Betsy was twelve the winter was colder than usual, and there was more illness.

Within a short time it seemed as if half the people of Philadelphia became ill with colds and sore throats. Every week there were fewer people on the streets, in the shops and the stores. Every week there were fewer Friends at meeting.

Of Betsy's sisters, Susan, Mary and Sarah went to help friends and relatives who were ill. Hannah, Rachel and Betsy were the only older girls left at home. Then Hannah and Rachel came down with sore throats. Only Betsy and her mother were left to do everything around the house.

Every day Betsy hurried home from school to
help her mother. She helped with the cleaning
and washing and cooking . She helped take care
of the younger children. She helped nurse Hannah and Rachel. At night she dropped into bed,
too tired to think.

One night Betsy woke to find her mother bend-
ing over her bed. Mrs. Griscom was holding a
candle in one hand. She was shaking Betsy with
the other hand. "Betsy! Betsy! Wake up!
Wake up! Thy father is ill, too. He woke suddenly with a very high fever. We should have
the doctor right away."

Mrs. Griscom looked down at Betsy. She
spoke quickly. "I hate to send thee out on a cold
night like this. But I'm afraid to wait until morning for the doctor. There's no one to go but
thee—I'm afraid to leave Father. Take George.
He'll keep thee company. It's a long way. Dress

warmly. Come, child, get up. There's no time to lose."

Betsy rubbed her eyes. Slowly she began to understand what her mother was saying. She jumped out of bed and pulled on her clothes.

Betsy could feel her heart beating faster and faster. Her father was *never* ill. He was always the first one up in the morning, the last one in bed at night. She couldn't imagine her father ill in bed like Hannah and Rachel.

Betsy had never dressed so quickly before. A few seconds later she was in George's room. "George! George! Wake up!"

George said, "I hear thee, Betsy," and went back to sleep again.

"George!" Betsy shook him. "George! Get up!"

Finally George opened his eyes. He listened. He tried to understand what Betsy was saying. He blinked. Then he sat up very straight. Now

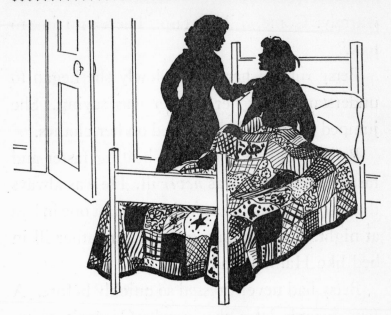

George blinked his eyes and sat up straight.

at last he was awake. He began to scramble into his clothes.

A few minutes later Betsy and George were standing in the hallway with their mother. Mrs. Griscom tied shawls around their heads and pulled their scarves a little tighter. "It's bitter cold outside," she said. "I hate for thee to go.

It is very far to Spruce Street." She turned to Betsy. "Thee knows where the doctor lives?" she asked.

Betsy nodded. "I'll know the house when I see it. Don't worry, Mother. We'll find him. We'll bring him back as soon as we can."

They opened the front door. "Oh!" Betsy couldn't keep from gasping. The cold air cut against her face like a knife. Her cheeks stung. Tears came to her eyes. It was hard to see. It was hard to breathe.

The hard snow crunched beneath their feet. Everything looked strange and different. There were no streets or walks or yards—only snow and houses.

Betsy had never been out so late before. The cold snowy night was exciting. Suddenly she felt wide awake. "Come on," she said again. "Let's run."

Just then they saw the night watchman

Betsy and George saw the night watchman.

ahead of them. He held a large lantern in his left hand and a big bell in his right. "Nine o'clock," he called as he rang the bell. "Nine o'clock and all is well!"

"Nine o'clock!" Betsy laughed. "Oh, George, I thought it was the middle of the night. I can't believe it. Why, I thought it was twelve, at least."

The hard snow crunched beneath their feet.

George nodded. He still looked half asleep. He was having a hard time keeping up with Betsy.

As they passed the State House, Betsy looked up at the belfry. Through the archways she could make out the faint outlines of the bell. How beautiful it looked against the starry sky!

Once more she could hear Dr. Franklin saying, "I'm glad you and the 'Liberty' bell are twins. It's a nice kind of twin to have."

On and on they ran. They went up one deserted street and down another. At last they came to Walnut Street and Betsy stopped suddenly. The doctor lived in this part of Philadelphia, she knew, but where was Spruce Street? Where was his house?

She looked up and down the street. No one was in sight. There was no one to ask the way. Were they lost?

Betsy closed her eyes. She tried to remember how the streets looked in the daylight. She tried to remember how the streets looked with all the snow gone. "We're on Walnut Street," she mumbled. "The doctor lives on Spruce."

Then she opened her eyes. "Spruce Street," she said, holding George's hand tighter. "I know where it is now. Come on, George. We aren't lost after all."

"Were we lost?" George looked at her in surprise.

She smiled at him. "Only for a minute," she said. "But it's all right now. I know the way."

Betsy and George hurried on. They hadn't been in this part of Philadelphia often, and they had never been here at night. But now that they were on Spruce Street, Betsy knew the way.

When they finally reached the doctor's house, they were glad to find that he was awake. Betsy started to tell him about her father.

"Come in. Come in," the doctor interrupted. "Not another word until you come in and warm yourselves by the fire. You look nearly frozen." He led them to the sitting room.

Betsy and George stumbled over to the fireplace and sank down gratefully on the settle. The doctor listened carefully as Betsy told him about her father. "Stay close by the fire while I harness the horses to the sleigh," he said. "It won't take long."

In a few minutes the doctor's wife came in with two large mugs. She handed one to Betsy and one to George. Hot milk! They thought nothing had ever tasted so good.

By the time they had finished the milk the doctor was in the driveway. "Up we go!" He helped them into the sleigh. "Giddap!" He cracked his whip. They went racing through the snowy streets.

The horses ran faster and faster. The sleigh skimmed over the snow. It seemed to Betsy that she and George had run for hours through the streets. Now, in a few minutes, they were home again.

A little later Betsy saw the doctor coming down the hall. "I've given your father some

The sleigh skimmed over the snow.

137

medicine," he said. "He's resting much better now. I believe his fever will be down by morning. I'm sure he's going to be all right."

"Oh!" Betsy was so happy she could scarcely speak. She smiled up at the doctor. Suddenly her knees felt very weak.

The doctor took her arm. "You'd better go to bed yourself," he said. "You've had a hard evening. You don't want to be ill, too."

Betsy was glad to do as he said. She hurried to her room and began to undress.

She was just ready to climb into bed when she saw the night watchman coming down the street. When he got directly in front of their house he rang his bell. Then he called out in his high, clear voice, "Ten o'clock! Ten o'clock and all is well!"

Ten o'clock! Had it been only one hour since she and George left home? It seemed impossible that so much could have happened in one hour.

Betsy stood at the window for a few minutes. She thought again of all that had happened. She felt as if she had been to the ends of the earth and back again. What a strange, unbelievable hour it had been! But if her father was all right, everything was all right.

"Ten o'clock," she repeated as she climbed into bed. "Ten o'clock and all is well."

The next day Betsy went from one task to another as fast as she could. There was so much to do. She and her mother didn't stop for a minute all day.

At five o'clock Betsy fixed trays for her father and Hannah and Rachel. Then she fed the two younger children and put them to bed. Now, at last, Betsy and her mother and George were ready to eat.

Betsy put three plates on the table. She put on three knives and forks and spoons. She put on three mugs. Then she stared at the table.

How strange it looked! How bare! How lonesome! The big table looked as if it, too, missed all the family.

The week passed slowly for Betsy. Then, on the following Monday, Mary came back. Four days later Sarah returned. By the end of the week Susan was home, too. Day by day Mr. Griscom, Hannah and Rachel grew a little stronger.

Two weeks later every member of the Griscom family sat down at the table together. How wonderful it was to be together again!

After supper Betsy looked at the big stack of dirty dishes. "Oh, Mary," she cried, "look at them! Aren't they beautiful?"

"Beautiful?" Mary stared at the dishes. What

was Betsy talking about. "What is beautiful, Betsy?" she asked.

"Why, the dirty dishes," said Betsy. "I think they're just beautiful."

The dirty dishes? Mary stared at her sister. Was she going to be ill, too. Was she ill already? Did she have chills and fever?

Betsy laughed at her sister's surprised look. "Eleven dirty plates," she said. "Eleven dirty mugs. Eleven dirty knives and forks and spoons. They're beautiful, Mary. It means the family is all together again. Oh, Mary, I missed all of thee so. I didn't think I'd ever enjoy washing a lot of dirty dishes, but tonight it seems wonderful."

Mary laughed. "Thee silly," she said. "Thee silly, silly, silly! But it's wonderful to be back, too. I guess thee's right. Dirty dishes can be rather nice. Come on silly. I'll help thee wash them."

XI

THE CONTEST

ONE EVENING in December Betsy was strangely silent. She was sitting in front of the big fireplace with Sarah, Mary and Susan. They were all sewing.

Usually Betsy kept everyone amused with her stories. Tonight she had nothing to say.

After half an hour of silence, Sarah looked up. "Betsy," she said, "doesn't thee feel well?"

Betsy bent her head lower over her sewing. "Of course I feel well," she said. "Why?"

Sarah shook her head. "I don't know. Usually thee is such a chatterbox. Thee has not said a word all evening."

"I feel very well," Betsy answered, but there was a quiver in her voice.

Sarah looked up. She saw that Betsy's eyes were filled with tears.

"Why, Betsy!" Sarah dropped her sewing. She ran to her sister's side. "Betsy, something *is* wrong. What is the matter with thee?"

"It's nothing." Betsy rubbed her eyes with the back of her hand. "Really 'tis nothing. I'm silly and foolish. I should be ashamed of myself. And I am." Suddenly she put her head on the arm of her chair and began to cry.

Betsy's sisters gathered around her.

All three sisters were around her now. They asked a dozen questions. Betsy was always so cheerful. She never cried. What was wrong?

Betsy sat up. She wiped her eyes. "Oh, dear," she said, " 'tis really so silly! I'm ashamed. It's just——" Betsy almost started to cry again. "It's just that they are going to have a great fair at the High Street Market four months from now."

Betsy's three sisters looked at one another. A fair wasn't something to cry over! What had happened to their little sister?

"But Betsy!" Sarah clapped her hands together. "That's wonderful news. Fairs are such fun. We'll all go. 'Tis very exciting."

"At the fair," Betsy went on slowly, "they are going to have an exhibit of handiwork."

"But they always do!" Sarah was more puzzled than ever. One didn't cry about handiwork exhibits either.

Again Betsy went on. "There are going to be

judges. They are going to give prizes for the three finest pieces of needlework."

"Why, Betsy, that's splendid." Susan's eyes were shining. "What a chance for thee! Thee has won every sewing contest they've had at school since thee has been there."

Betsy shook her head. "This isn't a school contest. This is for anyone in Philadelphia."

Mary laughed. "That shouldn't bother thee, Betsy. Thee will be fourteen next month and Mother says thee can sew better than she can. In fact, Mother says thee does finer needlework than anyone she knows. Thee has a good chance to win the contest. Why is thee crying?"

Betsy spoke slowly, as if she were explaining something to very small children. "Anyone in Philadelphia may enter," she said. "Thee knows as well as I do what things will be exhibited. There will be beautiful evening gowns. There will be lovely afternoon dresses. There will be handsome bedspreads. There will be wonderful quilts."

Betsy paused and sighed. "What can I enter? We don't need more bedclothes just now. Shall I make a plain white bonnet? Shall I make a Quaker skirt with four straight seams? Shall I make a Quaker bodice?"

"But, Betsy, surely the judges will look at the sewing," Sarah said gently. "The designs or the patterns shouldn't be too important. After all, it is a *sewing* contest. It's the sewing they'll judge."

Susan smiled. "And no one can take smaller stitches than thee, Betsy—no one in all Philadelphia. I'm sure of that."

Betsy shook her head again. "A man from the market came to school this morning. He told us all about the exhibit. He said we should make something different. Something original. Something that would make people say, 'Oh, how

lovely!' What can I sew that would make anyone say, 'Oh, how lovely!'?"

Betsy's three sisters were silent. They sus-
pected she was right. What chance would plain
Quaker things have in such a contest?

Betsy wiped her eyes again. "I know 'tis foolish for me to care. I know 'tis wrong and
worldly. But I can't help it. I'd work as hard as
anyone. I'm sure I would. But I haven't a
chance. What could a Quaker girl make?"

Sarah looked around the big room. It was
clean and neat. Each piece of furniture shone
from hard use and hard rubbing. But there was
no decoration of any kind. Everything seemed
to be something useful.

Then Sarah's glance caught something hanging on the wall—a small sampler. Betsy had
made it when she was six years old.

Sarah studied it for a long time. Here was

something without a use. "Thee could make a sampler for the exhibit, Betsy."

"A sampler?" Betsy laughed. Was her sister serious? "Why, Sarah, samplers are made by little girls when they are just beginning to learn to sew. What chance would a sampler have in a contest like this?"

"Thee could make a special sampler—a different one—a large one—a beautiful one." Sarah's eyes had a faraway look. "Betsy, thee could make one of the most beautiful samplers in all the world."

Betsy laughed again. "I may sew nicely, and thee is very kind to say so. But I know I could never do that."

"Why not?" Sarah opened her eyes wide. "Why not, Betsy? Sometime someone somewhere has to make the most beautiful thing of its kind in all the world."

"Sometime. Somewhere. Someone." Betsy

repeated the words slowly. Could the time be now? Could the place be Philadelphia? Could the one be she? For a few minutes Betsy's eyes sparkled.

Then she became solemn again. "I couldn't make a big, beautiful sampler," she said. "Thee knows I couldn't. Father and Mother would think it was a great waste of good time and good material."

Once more the four girls were silent. Her sisters knew Betsy was right. A large, fancy sampler would be worldly and wasteful.

The big clock on the mantel ticked slowly. All thoughts were on the contest, but for a long time no one could think of anything to say.

At last Sarah asked, "What are the prizes, Betsy?"

Betsy looked up from her sewing. "The first prize is five pounds, the second three pounds, the third one pound."

Sarah's eyes flashed. "We'll just have to think of something," she said. "We'll just have to." She looked at the sampler again. At the bottom Betsy had stitched in crooked little-girl stitches the words, "NEVER PUT OFF TILL TOMORROW WHAT YOU CAN DO TODAY."

"Betsy!" Sarah was so excited she jumped out of her chair and ran to her sister's side. "Betsy, I have another idea! Maybe it's a good one this time. If thee would use a quotation from the Bible on your sampler, Father and Mother might not object to it."

"Of course!" Susan cried. "It wouldn't be just a decoration then. The other day Father said that we should always keep the words of the Bible before our eyes."

"But Father didn't mean that literally," Mary said. "He didn't mean we should have our walls covered with words."

"Of course he didn't," Sarah said eagerly.

"He meant we should always follow the Bible's teaching. But this would be a way to have the words of the Bible really and truly before our eyes."

"Oh!" Betsy stared at her sister for a second. Then she threw her arms around Sarah's neck. "Oh, that's indeed a grand idea. A grand——" She stopped suddenly and looked very serious. "I just hope," she added slowly, "that Father thinks it is a grand idea, too."

XII

THE QUOTATION

THE NEXT morning Betsy told her father all about the contest. Then she told him about the girls' idea for a sampler.

When she had finished, Mr. Griscom looked very serious. "Thee knows, Betsy, that we Quakers believe we serve God best by leading quiet, simple lives. We do not believe in ornaments of any kind."

Betsy held her breath.

"Good words do not need decoration," Mr. Griscom went on slowly. "If they speak the truth, that is enough. However, I do not think it would be amiss if a quotation from the Bible were hung on the wall where all could see it."

"Oh, Father!" cried Betsy.

"And if thee wishes to make a design with thy

152

needle and thread I do not think that would be amiss either."

"Oh, thank thee, Father!" Betsy felt like jumping up and down, but she knew that would not be proper. She decided to curtsy instead. "Thank thee *very* much, Father," she repeated.

"Betsy."

"Yes, Father?"

"Has thee chosen the quotation yet?"

"No, Father."

Mr. Griscom took a large Bible off the shelf and handed it to Betsy. "It is filled with many wonderful thoughts," he said. "Thee should have no trouble making a choice."

Betsy sat down and opened the Bible. What quotation should she choose? The Bible was so big. There were so many books. Each book had so many chapters. Each chapter had so many verses. Her father had said it would not be hard to choose. She found it very hard.

Betsy turned the pages of the Bible slowly. The first book was Genesis. Many of the verses seemed right, but not exactly right.

The second book was Exodus. Betsy shook her head. She was sure if she looked long enough she would find a very special verse— one that was just right for her.

The third book was Leviticus. Leviticus! Suddenly she knew what she wanted. Betsy felt very excited and happy. Her eyes skimmed the pages quickly now. Where was the verse? She couldn't remember.

Finally she came to Chapter Twenty-five. She glanced down at the verses quickly. Number ten—there it was. It was like finding an old friend. It stood out from the page as if it were printed in different ink.

Betsy read the words slowly to herself, even though she knew them by heart: "Proclaim

liberty throughout all the land unto all the inhabitants thereof."

That was the verse she wanted. That was the
verse for her sampler. The more Betsy thought
about it the more excited she became.

Closing her eyes, she could see the sampler
just as she wanted it to be. There would be a
picture of the big bell in the center. Around the
edge, just as on the bell itself, she would put
the quotation. And just as it was on the bell, she
would put the date, too: 1752—the year she was
born and the bell was made.

Suddenly Betsy didn't care whether she won
the prize or not. It was the sampler now, not
the prize, that was important to her.

XIII

THE SAMPLER

NEXT EVENING the whole family was sitting around the big fireplace. Outside the wind whistled and howled. Inside the fire burned bright.

Such a bright fire needed a lot of wood. Before long the wood box was empty. George looked at it and made a face. He would have to fill it again.

"Brrrrrr!" He shivered. He didn't want to leave the warm, cheerful fire. He put on his heavy coat and wrapped a big shawl around his head. Then he picked up the wood basket and went outside.

When he came back again he was smiling. "I'm glad I went to get the wood," he said. "It's a beautiful night—clear and cold. The stars and the moon are shining. 'Tis like the night we went for the doctor. Remember, Betsy?"

Betsy smiled. "Of course I remember. I remember how black the big belfry looked against the dark-blue sky, how bright the stars were, and——"

Suddenly Betsy stopped. "George," she cried, "that's the way I'm going to make my sampler! I'll have the big bell ringing out in the night. I'll make a dark-blue sky filled with stars. The moon will shine on the bell so thee can read the words. They'll stand out in the moonlight like . . . like the stars."

The next day Betsy started to work on her sampler. First she combed the wool until it was smooth. Next she spun it into yarn. Then she dyed the yarn all the colors she would need. Finally she was ready to weave the cloth.

But this was only the beginning. The design itself took much more time.

Every evening Betsy sat on the hearth and made sketches with a piece of charcoal. Somehow the sketches never quite satisfied her. Sometimes the bell was too big, sometimes too small. There were too many stars, or too few stars. There was too much moonlight and then there was too little.

One evening Betsy at last drew a sketch that seemed almost perfect. This time the bell was the right size. There was just the right number of stars and just enough moonlight.

But the stars themselves weren't quite right yet. Betsy had drawn their six points all straight and even, but she thought they looked stiff and strange.

"The bell seems to ring," she thought. "But the stars don't twinkle."

Betsy worked and worked and worked, but she couldn't get the stars to satisfy her. She didn't know what to do. "Spring will be here," she said, "before I've even started to embroider the sampler."

One evening Mrs. Griscom looked down at Betsy's sketches. "Thee could try five-pointed stars," she suggested. "Perhaps they would look more like real stars."

Betsy was delighted. "That's a good idea, Mother. I'll try them right away."

But Betsy soon found that five-pointed stars were hard to make. The first one was lopsided. The second was top-heavy. The third was too skinny. The fourth was too fat. No matter what she did she couldn't make all the points the same length and the same width.

Finally Betsy took the sketches to her mother. "I've tried and tried," she said. "I just can't make a five-pointed star."

Mrs. Griscom looked up from her sewing. "Why, a five-pointed star is easy."

"Easy!" Betsy stared at her mother.

Her mother reached into her sewing basket. "I guess I have never showed thee how to do it." She took out a piece of cloth and her scissors. She cut a small square.

"Now watch carefully." Mrs. Griscom folded the square in half. Then she folded the lower

"Now watch carefully," Mrs. Griscom said.

half up at an angle. Next she folded the lower
edge to the upper edge and then folded the upper

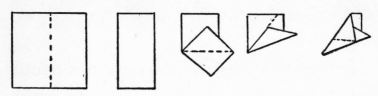

   1.   **2.**   **3.**   **4.**   **5. & 6.**

section down over the lower section. *Snip!* One
small corner of the folded cloth fell into her lap.
She handed the other piece to Betsy.

Very carefully Betsy unfolded it. "Mother!"
She couldn't believe her eyes. There in the palm
of her hand lay a perfect little five-pointed star.
"Oh, Mother," she cried, "It's wonderful!
Where did thee learn such a thing?"

Mrs. Griscom smiled. "My mother showed
it to me," she said. "She learned it from her
mother, who had learned it from her mother.
Perhaps someday thee will teach it to thy own
little daughters."

Betsy looked down at the little star again. Now everything was perfect. Now she could get ahead with her sampler.

The real work began. The ground appeared first, and then the sky. Soon there was a cloud, and then another and another.

One by one the little five-pointed stars began to twinkle in the sky. Betsy liked working on these best of all. They were so small and delicate. They reminded her of jewels on ladies' dresses.

Then the big bell began to appear, bit by bit. Finally it too was finished. Only the words were left to be done.

When Betsy finished embroidering them they looked as if someone had drawn them there with a fine pen. But, fine as they were, they could be read easily. They stood out clear and strong on the big bell.

Now at last the sampler was finished!

XIV

BOOTHS FOR THE FAIR

EVERY AFTERNOON on her way home from school, Betsy stopped at the High Street Market. It was a busy place now. There was always something new to see. Workmen rushed back and forth. There were sawing and pounding and hammering. Platforms appeared. Booths sprang up, one after the other. There was excitement everywhere.

One day Hannah and Betsy stood beside the needlework booth. The workmen were putting on the finishing touches and it looked very grand.

"Just think, Betsy," said Hannah, "soon thy sampler will be hanging in that booth. Won't thee be proud?"

"But perhaps they won't hang it." Betsy looked very solemn.

"Won't hang it?" Hannah stared at her sister. "Why wouldn't they?"

"Thee knows they don't hang everything," Betsy answered. "They pick only the best. Perhaps they won't think my sampler is good enough."

"Fie!" Hannah tossed her head. "They'll put it right out in front. Wait and see."

But as they walked home Hannah was quiet. The Griscoms had all been so sure Betsy would win—everyone but Betsy. Was Betsy right? After all, it was a big exhibit. Most of the things were made by grown women. Did Betsy have a chance? Hannah began to wonder.

It seemed to Betsy and her sisters that April would never end. The hammering and pounding at the High Street Market seemed louder now. The workmen worked faster. Big signs appeared on the fences and lampposts: "THE

HIGH STREET FAIR—SPECIAL EXHIBITS—GRAND
PRIZES—STARTING MAY THE FIRST."

On the first of May Betsy carried her sampler
down to the needlework booth. She thought the
booth looked larger than ever. The man standing inside looked large, too. Betsy felt especially
small. She wished she had never thought of the
exhibit.

"Yes, my little maid?" The man looked down
at Betsy. "You wanted something?"

"I . . . I . . ." Betsy felt smaller and smaller.
"I have a sampler here. 'Tis for the exhibit."

The man smiled. Betsy thought he was laughing at her. Her cheeks grew red.

Without glancing at the sampler the man
picked it up and tossed it onto a shelf. Then he
picked up a quill and a small piece of paper.
"Name?" he asked.

Tears came to Betsy's eyes. She wanted to
stamp her foot. She wanted to take her sampler

"Name?" the man asked.

and run home with it. It might not be worth hanging up, but the man had no right to throw it around like an old piece of cloth.

"Name?" The man looked at Betsy impatiently.

Betsy cleared her throat and blinked. She wouldn't let him see that she was angry and about to cry.

When she finally spoke, her voice was loud and clear. "Betsy Griscom," she answered.

"Age?"

"Fourteen."

"Address?"

"Mulberry Street near Fourth."

The man pinned the paper on her sampler. "They're hanging the things tomorrow," he said. "If your sampler isn't hung you're supposed to come and get it that afternoon."

Betsy hurried home. She didn't want to think about her sampler or the exhibit. She didn't even want to think about the fair—not until tomorrow, anyway.

XV

TODAY IS TOMORROW

Betsy opened her eyes. She sat up in bed. "Hannah!" Betsy shook her sister. "Hannah, wake up! 'Tis tomorrow."

Hannah rubbed her eyes sleepily. "It can't be tomorrow. 'Tis today."

"Silly!" Betsy laughed. "Does thee not know that today is tomorrow?"

Hannah rubbed her eyes again. "I'm still half asleep," she said, "and I think thee is, too. Such a way to talk."

Betsy jumped out of bed. "Well, the man said to come back tomorrow. That's today. So today is tomorrow. Get up! Get up, Hannah! Doesn't thee want to go to the fair?"

"The fair!" Hannah was out of bed in a second. "It's today, Betsy! Oh, isn't it exciting?

168

Dear me, we must hurry. There's so much to do before we go."

By two o'clock in the afternoon all the housework was finished. Now Betsy and her sisters could get ready for the fair. George was excited too. He even put on his best suit and slicked down his hair without being told. "Not ready yet?" he asked. "I'm going now. I'll meet thee there."

" 'Tis like First Day," said Rachel. "It seems strange to be putting on our best clothes this afternoon."

As they got close to the fair Betsy walked slower and slower. She wanted to go to the needlework booth. But she certainly didn't want to ask the man for her sampler and see him smile as he handed it back to her.

Then she saw George pushing through the crowd toward her as fast as he could.

"Betsy! Betsy!" His coat was off. His collar was unbuttoned. His hair looked as if it had never been combed. "Betsy! Thee should see it!"

"George!" Betsy grabbed his arm. "Stop shouting! Stand still! What's the matter? What happened?"

" 'Tis there, Betsy. I saw it."

"What's where?"

George was breathing so hard he could scarcely talk. "I ran all the way. I've been to the needlework booth, Betsy. And thy sampler is hanging right out in front where everyone can see it."

Betsy forgot she was fourteen years old and supposed to act like a young lady. She took George's hand and began to run.

They ran in and out among the people, between the booths and around the vendors. Finally they came to the front of the needlework booth.

"Isn't it beautiful?" George said.

"Oh!" Betsy stared at the sampler as if she had never seen it before.

"Isn't it beautiful?" George looked first at the sampler and then at his sister. "It's the most beautiful thing in the whole exhibit."

Betsy looked around quickly. "Hush, George, someone might hear thee. The sampler does look nice and I'm glad I made it. But 'tis far from being the most beautiful piece."

George's eyes flashed. "*I* think it is," he said.

Betsy smiled at him. "Thee says that just because I'm thy sister."

"No, I do not." George looked very serious. "It is the most beautiful, no matter who made it."

"Thee is a boy," Betsy answered, "and boys don't know about such things. See that beautiful evening gown up there? It's elegant. I'm sure it will win first prize."

"Well, I'm a boy, all right," George said flatly, "and I may not know about such things. But I know what I like and I know what I think is pretty. The sampler is the prettiest thing here."

"Hush!" Betsy cried. "People will hear thee."

"I don't care who hears me say it. I'm going to say it as loud as I please."

"Hush! Hush, please!" Betsy's cheeks were getting redder and redder. "Everyone is staring at thee."

"I don't care." George was really shouting now.

Betsy tried to look serious, but the corners of her mouth refused to stay down. George looked so funny standing there talking about her sampler at the top of his voice. "Here come our sisters. We'll see what they think!"

The girls all praised the sampler again and again. But they had to agree with Betsy that the evening gown would surely win first prize.

The afternoon passed quickly. There was so

much to see and so much to do. They had to
make every minute count.

When the State House bell began to ring,
Betsy and her sisters and George were at the far
end of the fairgrounds.

"Oh!" Betsy looked up startled. " 'Tis five
o'clock already. That's when they're going to
award the prizes at the needlework booth."

They tried to make their way through the
crowd as quickly as possible. It seemed as if
everyone in Philadelphia had come to the fair.

When they got twenty feet from the needlework booth the press of people was worse than
ever. "Oh, dear!" Betsy stopped and looked
around her. "We'll never get close enough to
hear. We can't even see." She stood on tiptoe
and tried to look over the heads of the people.
"We should have come back here much earlier."

"It's too late to do anything about it now,"
George said. He jumped up and down. When

he was up he could catch a glimpse of the plat-form. When he was down he could tell them what he had seen.

"There's a table up there," he said. "Four men are sitting around it. Now one is getting up and walking to the center of the platform. He's talking but I can't make out what he's saying."

George continued to jump up and down. "The man has taken down that evening gown thee were admiring. He's holding it up for everyone to see. He's talking again.

"Now a lady's walking up on the stage. I guess she's the one who made the gown. Yes, she did. The man's handing her the prize."

"See?" Betsy looked at George and smiled. "Didn't we tell thee the gown would win? Boys just don't understand about such things."

"I still think thy sampler better than that fussy old dress," George said firmly. "Who'd want to wear it anyway? That skirt's so full I don't see how anyone could get into a carriage with it on."

He jumped up again. "Well, the lady's left the platform and the man's talking. Now he's taking down a big quilt."

Betsy nodded her head. She had noticed a particularly well-made quilt on display. If that was the one George was talking about, it certainly deserved the second prize.

Now the second lady was on the platform receiving her prize. Betsy stood on tiptoe but she couldn't see her. "Oh, dear." She settled back on her heels again. "I'll be glad when this is over! I've stretched my neck so much I'm sure it must be an inch longer."

"Betsy! Betsy!" George shouted.

Betsy stared at him. "I'm right beside thee. Thee doesn't have to yell."

"Oh, Betsy!" George whispered this time. "Thee should see what the man is doing now!"

Betsy stood on tiptoe again and stretched her head as high as she could. This time she caught a quick glimpse of the platform. Suddenly she covered her mouth with her hand and said softly, "Oh, no! It can't be!"

"But it is. It is!" George was shouting again. " 'Tis thy sampler. Thee has won third prize."

Betsy had never felt so frightened in her life. She looked at George and her sisters. "I can't go up there," she said. "I can't push through this big crowd of people with everyone staring at me. I can't go up on that platform all alone."

Suddenly she smiled. "I'll just pretend I'm not here. If none of us says anything no one will know the difference. I can get the prize tomorrow. They didn't say we had to be here. I——"

"Betsy Griscom!" Hannah shook her gently. "Of course thee is going up there. Such nonsense! Thee should be proud to go. It's a won-

derful honor. Now hurry. They're all waiting
for thee."

Betsy never knew how she got through the
crowd and onto the platform. She pretended she
was walking with her eyes closed. Somehow she
felt that if she didn't look at anyone, no one
would look at her.

The man in the center of the platform smiled
at Betsy. Then he congratulated her and handed
her the prize.

Betsy looked down at the money in her hand.
It wasn't one pound. It was five pounds!

Betsy looked up quickly. "Thee has made a
mistake," she said. "The third prize was to be
one pound. Thee has given me five!"

"Third prize?" The man looked at her, as-
tonished. "You didn't win third prize," he said.
"You won first prize."

"First prize?" Betsy couldn't believe it. "But
those other prizes—the gown and the quilt. I

thought—— We couldn't hear what thee said. But I was sure——"

The man smiled at her. "The gown won third prize," he said, "and the quilt second. You see, we always save the best for the last. If you remember," he went on, "when we announced the contest we said that prizes were to be given to the most original pieces. We all thought that your sampler was perfectly made and the most unusual piece in the whole exhibit."

He pointed at the gown and the quilt. "They're beautiful, of course, but the gown was copied from a French fashion and the quilt is an English design. We like your sampler because it is an American design made from American materials. America must learn to develop her own arts. Your sampler is a good beginning."

Betsy curtsied. "Thank thee. Thank thee very much." She couldn't say more.

Once again Betsy found her way through the

crowd. Finally she was standing beside George and her sisters. Without a word she opened her hand and showed them the gold pieces.

George was the first to understand what had happened. "Thee won first prize!" He began to laugh. "So boys don't know about such things. What a pity! And the four judges were men. I suppose men don't know about such things, either."

It was late when they finally started home. The moon was high in the sky and the stars were shining. As they passed the State House, Betsy looked up and smiled. The stars seemed close and friendly. They looked as if they were almost touching the big belfry. "They *do* look five-pointed." She laughed. "I'm glad I made them five-pointed on my sampler."

XVI

A FAMOUS STORY

RUTH and Jim Wills walked along the streets of Philadelphia. They had come to visit their aunt and now they were sight-seeing.

"You know," Ruth said, "whenever I walk around Philadelphia I always feel as if I'm bumping into pages of a history book everywhere I go."

"Well, you'd better watch out then," Jim said, "because you're about to bump into one right now. There's Betsy Ross's house just across the street."

"Oh, Jim, how nice!" Ruth stopped and looked at the little house. "Let's go in, shall we?"

They crossed the street and stood for a few minutes looking at the two-story house with the little attic. Then they opened the door and looked in.

"Good morning." A woman came toward them. "I'm Mrs. Stewart," she said. "Won't you come in? You're our first visitors today. I unlocked the door just a few minutes ago."

"We're Ruth and Jim Wills," Ruth said. "Are you sure we're not too early?" she asked.

"Oh, no." Mrs. Stewart smiled at them. "But it's nice you've come early. This is our busy season and sometimes this room gets very crowded. You see, over 150,000 people visit this house every year. Some days we have so many visitors there's scarcely room for everyone."

Jim looked around the little room. "Has the house always been just like this," he asked, "ever since Betsy Ross lived here?"

Mrs. Stewart shook her head. "No," she said, "other people lived in the house after Betsy Ross died. Then in 1898 many important people from all over the United States organized the American Flag House and Betsy Ross Memorial.

They bought the house for a historical landmark.

"In 1937," Mrs. Stewart went on, "the house was restored to its original condition by Mr. Atwater Kent. Now the people of Philadelphia are very proud of it. They think it is fortunate that this house of hers has been preserved."

Ruth smiled. "I can't remember when I first heard that Betsy Ross made the first flag," she said. "It seems to me I've known that story as long as I've known my own name. But I haven't any idea how she happened to make it. Was she a flagmaker? Had she made any flags before she made the Stars and Stripes?"

Mrs. Stewart shook her head. "She said she never had."

"Then how did she happen to make it?" Ruth asked. "Would they ask someone who had never made a flag to make such an important one?"

"Well, you see," Mrs. Stewart began, "as Betsy Griscom she had made quite a name for herself for fine sewing. Even when she was in school she won many honors at exhibits and at the High Street fairs. She was often asked to make designs for quilts, and was known for her artistic ability.

"When she married John Ross," Mrs. Stewart went on, "he was working in an upholsterer's shop. Then, after they were married, they opened a little shop of their own."

Mrs. Stewart glanced around the room. "The little shop was right here," she said, "and business was brisk from the very start. I think it is easy to believe that Betsy Ross, well known in Philadelphia for her sewing, might have been chosen to make the first flag.

"But that isn't all," Mrs. Stewart added. "There's another reason why she might have been chosen. Betsy's husband John Ross had an uncle named Colonel George Ross. He was a very close friend of General George Washington and——"

At that moment the door opened and a dignified, gray-haired lady came in.

"Oh, how nice!" Mrs. Stewart hurried to meet her. Then, turning to Ruth and Jim, she said, "This will be a very pleasant surprise for you. I want you to meet Miss Edna Randolph Worrell. She is the great-great-grandniece of Betsy Ross.

"Miss Worrell, this is Ruth and Jim Wills. I was just going to tell them the story that is told of the making of the first flag. I know it would mean much more if you would tell it to them."

Miss Worrell smiled. "I've told it many, many times," she said, "but I always enjoy telling it again. When I was a little girl my grandmother Mrs. Susan Turner used to tell us this story about her Aunt Betsy over and over again." Miss Worrell laughed. "Now I'm the storyteller in the family," she said.

Miss Worrell sat down in a low chair and

folded her hands. "Sit down," she said, "and let's pretend for a few minutes that we're back in Philadelphia in 1776."

Ruth and Jim smiled at each other. It wasn't hard, sitting in that little living room, to imagine how Philadelphia looked almost two hundred years before.

"It was June," said Miss Worrell, "and General Washington had come to Philadelphia from New York to talk to the members of Congress.

"There were many problems on his mind. He needed men to fight the British. Many supplies were lacking. The states were still divided among themselves and needed to be united.

"Most of the states and many of the ships were using their own emblems. General Washington felt that it was very important to have a national flag which could be used by both the army and the navy.

"One day General Washington, Mr. Robert

Morris and Colonel George Ross discussed this
new flag for the new country. General Washington had drawn a design and was eager to have
someone make it. . . . Is it not easy to believe
that Colonel Ross would suggest his own niece,
especially since she was well known in Philadelphia for her sewing?"

Miss Worrell leaned back and closed her eyes.
"Now let's come back here to the little shop,"
she said. "It was early in the morning and Mrs.
Betsy Ross was getting her place ready for another busy day. . . . I can just see her dusting the
furniture and sweeping the hearth. . . . Then
there was a knock at the door and she went to
answer it.

"Of course she expected to see a customer,"
Miss Worrell went on. "She certainly didn't
expect to see three of the most important men in
Philadelphia standing on her doorstep. There
was her husband's uncle, Colonel George Ross.

There was Mr. Robert Morris, one of the wealth-iest men in Pennsylvania. And most important of all there was General George Washington, who was so tall he had to stoop in order to enter the little shop.

"Betsy couldn't imagine why these important and busy men had come to her shop, but General Washington didn't keep her waiting long. He took a sheet of paper out of his pocket and showed her a sketch of a flag. Then he asked her if she thought she could make one like it out of bunting.

"Betsy Ross said she didn't know, but she would try.

"She looked at the design carefully. It had six white stripes and seven red ones. In the upper left-hand corner there was a blue field with a cluster of thirteen stars. Betsy guessed at once that the thirteen stars and stripes were for the thirteen new states.

"Then she noticed that the stars had six points. 'I think it is a beautiful design,' she said. 'There is one thing, however, which I would suggest. I believe the stars would look better if they were five-pointed.'

"The three men agreed, but General Washington said that a great many flags were needed very quickly, and he thought six-pointed stars would be easier to cut.

"Betsy smiled. She took up a small piece of cloth, folded it several times and cut it once with her scissors. Then, unfolding it, she showed the men a perfect five-pointed star.

"General Washington laughed. 'Well, if you can make five-pointed stars that quickly,' he said, 'I don't suppose we have to worry.'

"We know Betsy Ross made many flags after that," Miss Worrell went on. "There are records of money paid to her for flags, and bills for bunting made out in her own hand.

"Many people and many organizations have honored her through the years, and now we have this." Miss Worrell picked up a postage stamp and showed it to Ruth and Jim. "You see," she explained, "Betsy Ross was born on January 1, 1752. So on January 1, 1952, the United States Congress directed the Post Office Department to issue a Betsy Ross stamp in honor of the two-hundredth anniversary of her birth.

"See, it shows her displaying the new flag to General Washington, Robert Morris and George Ross. They are sitting here in this house. The design was taken from a painting by Charles H. Weisgerber, one of the founders and first secretary of the Memorial Association."

Ruth and Jim looked around the room. Outside the automobiles and buses rushed by. They could hear horns and the shrill scream of a siren. But inside the little house they felt very close to General Washington and Betsy Ross. It wasn't hard to believe that the first emblem of a great country had been made in this room. The people who had created it seemed very near.

Ruth smiled. "I told Jim that Philadelphia was like a big history book," she said. "Now I'm glad we came here first. I feel as if we've started on the very first page."

Jim nodded. "I just hope the other pages are as interesting," he said. "Come on, Ruth, we'd better go. We want to see the Liberty Bell and Independence Hall and——"

Miss Worrell smiled. "Betsy and the Liberty Bell were twins," she said. "They both arrived in the same year. And Betsy's father, Samuel Griscom, helped build the belfry of Independence Hall. They were called the State House and the State House Bell when she was a little girl, but she was right here in Philadelphia when they got their new names. She was a part of our early history in many different ways."

Ruth and Jim hurried down the street. It was nice knowing they weren't saying good-by to Betsy Ross. It would be fun hearing about her again and again as they read the history of old Philadelphia.